Granger Index

P9-AGV-100

The Poet's Tales

Also edited by William Cole

MAN'S FUNNIEST FRIEND: *The Dog in Stories,
Reminiscences, Poems, and Cartoons*

A CASE OF THE GIGGLES

BEASTLY BOYS AND GHASTLY GIRLS

THE BIRDS AND THE BEASTS WERE THERE

POEMS FOR SEASONS AND CELEBRATIONS

POEMS OF MAGIC AND SPELLS

I WENT TO THE ANIMAL FAIR

HUMOROUS POETRY FOR CHILDREN

Written by William Cole

FRANCES FACE-MAKER: A GOING-TO-BED BOOK

The Poet's Tales

A NEW BOOK OF STORY POEMS

Selected by William Cole

Illustrated by Charles Keeping

WORLD PUBLISHING

TIMES MIRROR

NEW YORK

Published by The World Publishing Company
Published simultaneously in Canada by
Nelson, Foster & Scott Ltd.
Library of Congress catalog card number: 72-101841
Copyright © 1971 by The World Publishing Company
Illustrations copyright © 1971 by Charles Keeping
Designed by Jack Jaget

WORLD PUBLISHING
TIMES MIRROR

COPYRIGHT ACKNOWLEDGMENTS

The editor and The World Publishing Company herewith render thanks to
the following authors, publishers, and agents whose interest, cooperation, and
permission to reprint have made possible the preparation of *The Poet's Tales:
A New Book of Story Poems*. All possible care has been taken to trace the
ownership of every selection included and to make full acknowledgment for its
use. If any errors have accidentally occurred, they will be corrected in subsequent
editions, provided notification is sent to the publisher.

A.B.P. International, for "The Dam" from *The Stone in the Midst*, by Patric
Dickinson, published by Methuen & Company, Ltd., London. Allans World of
Music for "The Bushrangers," from *Song for All Seasons*, by Edward Harrington,
reprinted by permission of Allans Music (Australia) Pty. Ltd., Melbourne. Angus
and Robertson Ltd., for "The Death of Ben Hall," from *Australian Bush Ballads*,
by William H. Ogilvie; for "Legend," from *The Gateway*, by Judith Wright,
Australian Poets Series: Judith Wright; and for "Robbing the Tree-Hive," from
Poems, by Ernest G. Moll. All published by Angus and Robertson Ltd. Atlantic,
Little, Brown and Company for "The Tale the Hermit Told," from *Oddments
Inklings Omens Moments*, by Alistair Reid, copyright 1954, © 1955, 1956, 1957,
1958, 1959. Reprinted by permission of Atlantic, Little, Brown and Company.
Scott Bates, for "The Fable of the Transcendent Tannenbaum," by Scott Bates,
from *The Carleton Miscellany*, copyright by Scott Bates. Reprinted by permission
of Carleton College. William Beyer, for his poem "The Trap," from *The New
Mexico Quarterly*. Reprinted by permission of the author. Brandt & Brandt, for
"Twin Lake Hunter," by A. B. Guthrie, Jr., from *Harper's Magazine*, copyright
1964 by Harper's Magazine, Inc. Reprinted by permission of Brandt & Brandt.
Coward-McCann, Inc., for "A Lady Comes to an Inn," from *The Creaking Stair*,
by Elizabeth Coatsworth, copyright 1923 by Elizabeth Coatsworth. Copyright
1929, 1949 by Coward-McCann, Inc. Reprinted by permission of Coward-Mc-
Cann, Inc. The Cresset Press Ltd., for "The Princess and the Gypsies," from
Collected Poems, by Frances Cornford. Reprinted by permission of The Cresset
Press Ltd. Delacorte Press, for "When I Brought the News," from *Meet My
Maker the Mad Molecule*, by J. P. Donleavy, copyright © 1954, 1955, 1956, 1959,
1960, 1961, 1963, 1964 by J. P. Donleavy. First published in *Playboy*. A Seymour
Lawrence Book/Delacorte Press. Reprinted by permission of Delacorte Press. Dodd,
Mead & Company, for "The Cremation of Sam McGee," from *The Collected Poems
of Robert Service*, by Robert Service. Reprinted by permission of Dodd, Mead &
Company and the Ryerson Press. Also Ernest Benn Ltd., for "The Cremation of
Sam McGee," from *Songs of a Sourdough*, by Robert Service. Reprinted by permission of Ernest Benn Ltd. Dodd, Mead & Company, for "A Nautical Extrava-
ganza" and "The Powerful Eyes o' Jeremy Tait," from *Nautical Lays of a Lands-
man*, by Wallace Irwin. Reprinted by permission of Dodd, Mead & Company,

[4]

Contents

CHARACTERS AND INDIVIDUALISTS

BIRDS, BEASTS, AND BUGS

ADVENTURES AND DISASTERS

LOVE STORIES

FIGHTING MEN

AT SEA

ODD AND FUNNY

Introduction

Twelve years ago I put together a collection of poetry which I called—and the title didn't strain my imagination—*Story Poems*. In the years since then, as I kept looking at other people's anthologies of poetry, I realized that there are certain poems that keep appearing and reappearing. They're nice poems, but you get sick of seeing them in every book you open; poems like "Paul Revere's Ride," and "The One-Hoss Shay" (properly known as "The Deacon's Masterpiece"), and "Casey at the Bat." Eventually poems like these get to be known as "old chestnuts," and I began to feel resentful that they were taking up space in my story poetry collection, especially since I had been gathering new and exciting story poems over the years. So finally I decided that the time had come to put together a new collection, dropping the chestnuts—fifteen long, long poems—and adding the new stuff (about seventy poems). And here it is.

The world's first poets were the storytellers. Long before man could write, and thousands of years before there were books, the hunters would gather around the fire after dark and the storyteller would recite the adventures of the day, or recount legends of their ancestors. These earliest stories were sung or chanted rhythmically. Later on there came the folk ballads, and the songs of the troubadours, who were paid to sing fine stories, usually exaggerated, about the heroism of their employers, the knights and nobles. Many of the early ballads have been passed down from generation to generation and we still hear them sung by today's folk singers; there are a few in this book.

As with anything else, there is an art in writing a good story in verse. A story poem points up the dramatic parts of a tale; the poet doesn't have time to fool around with setting the stage or describing the characters down to the last eyelash. He wants to tell a neat and complete and exciting (or funny) story in a way that keeps you bounding along with him, and in a way that gives you the feeling that you're there, right in the middle of the story that's unfolding. These, more than most poems, are fun to read aloud. Most of them have a rhythm, a regular beat, that sounds fine. Some of them are very dramatic; exciting things happen, and they should be read aloud with a great deal of hip-hip-hooray, in a let-yourself-go manner.

Some of the poetry in this book—well, let's be honest—most of the poetry in this book isn't great poetry. A story poem isn't personal; it doesn't bring out the intensity of feeling from the poet that a great poem does. He's telling a tale, and he's got to keep himself out of it, and keep his eye on the narrative. But some of the tales *are* great stories. And three of the great poets of our century, D. H. Lawrence, Thomas Hardy, and Robert Frost, are represented in their lighter moments. For this new book of story poems, I have added some poems that aren't really easy to understand at first reading—such as Alastair Reid's "The Tale the Hermit Told," and Conrad Aiken's "And in the Hanging Gardens." They'll give you a little to chew on, and that's to the good. I've also added some pretty odd things, May Swenson's "The Watch," for example, or J. P. Donleavy's prose poem, "When I Brought the News." Most of the poems are American or English, but there are also representatives from Australia, Ireland, Scotland, Wales, France, Sweden, and Germany. Canadians are in here, too, and among them is the poem I consider a fine discovery, Duncan Campbell Scott's "The Forsaken," which, when I first read it, gave me a genuine bodily chill, which is certainly a test of a real poem.

If there are poems in this collection that you particularly like, I wish you'd do what I did when I was first reading poetry: write the author's name down, and the next time you're in a library look for his books, or look for other things of his in other anthologies. To discover a good poet who is new to you is just like finding a new friend, a friend who will be with you for life.

As the English poet laureate, C. Day Lewis, says in his book *Poetry for You:* ". . . to learn poetry is to learn a respect for words; and without this respect for words, you will never be able to think clearly or express yourself properly: and until you can do that, you'll never fully grow up—not though you live to be a hundred."

William Cole

Strange
and Mysterious

The Unfortunate Miller

On windy days the mill
Turned with a will,
But on calm days it spread
Its four sails—dead.

The one-eyed miller man
Laments that ban,
And to the windless sky
Turning his vexed eye:

"God help," he sadly says,
"This business;
A hundred days and more
The wind's forebore,

"And lacking breezes I
Am bound to die;
The profit I've forgone
In offal and grist alone

"Would have bought a cock and a hen,
A gilt for my pen,
And a row of asters planted
Just where I wanted;

"But since the wind is still—
The devil take the mill!
Never it rains but pours—
Let's in-a-doors."

So in-a-doors goes he
To see—alas, to see—
Not the scrapings of a pan or pot
In his famished cot.

The tap of the clock indoors,
The dusty floors,
His empty crock and purse,
Made bad seem worse.

He looked at himself in the glass—
How thin he was!
He looked at the time and date—
Too late! Too late!

And creeping again to the mill
That stood stone still,
He tied round his neck the loop
Of a long dark rope,

Drove a tenpenny nail
Into the mill's black sail,
Hung his watch on a shelf,
Then hung himself.

And lo, the wind came! Beshrew,
How the wind blew!
And the sails, with the miller dying,
Went flying, flying.

A. E. COPPARD

The Fall of J. W. Beane

A GHOST STORY

In all the Eastern hemisphere
You wouldn't find a knight, a peer,
A viscount, earl or baronet,
A marquis or a duke, nor yet
A prince, or emperor, or king,
Or sultan, czar, or anything
That could in family pride surpass
J. Wentworth Beane of Boston, Mass.
His family tree could far outscale
The beanstalk in the fairy tale;
And Joseph's coat would pale before
The blazon'd coat-of-arms he bore,
The arms of his old ancestor,
One Godfrey Beane, "who crossed, you know,
About two hundred years ago."
He had it stamped, engraved, embossed,
Without the least regard to cost,
Upon his house, upon his gate,
Upon his tablecloth, his plate,
Upon his knocker, and his mat,
Upon his watch, inside his hat;
On scarfpin, handkerchief, and screen,
And cards; in short, J. Wentworth Beane
Contrived to have old Godfrey's crest
On everything that he possessed.
And lastly, when he died, his will
Proved to contain a codicil
Directing that a sum be spent
To carve it on his monument.

But if you think this ends the scene
You little know J. Wentworth Beane.

To judge him by the common host
Is reckoning without his ghost.
And it is something that befell
His ghost I chiefly have to tell.

At midnight of the very day
They laid J. Wentworth Beane away,
No sooner had the clock come round
To 12 P.M. than from the ground
Arose a spectre, lank and lean,
With frigid air and haughty mien;
No other than J. Wentworth Beane,
Unchanged in all, except his pride—
If anything, intensified.

He looked about him with that air
Of supercilious despair
That very stuck-up people wear
At some society affair
When no one in their set is there.
Then, after brushing from his sleeves
Some bits of mold and clinging leaves,
And lightly dusting off his shoe,
The iron gate he floated through,
Just looking back the clock to note,
As one who fears to miss a boat.
Ten minutes later found him on
The ghosts' Cunarder—*Oregon;*
And ten days later by spook time
He heard the hour of midnight chime
From out the tower of Beanley Hall,
And stood within the graveyard wall
Beside a stone, moss-grown and green,
On which these simple words were seen:

IN MEMORY
SIR GODFREY BEANE

The while he gazed in thought serene

A little ghost of humble mien,
Unkempt and crooked, bent and spare,
Accosted him with cringing air:
"Most noble sir, 'tis plain to see
You are not of the likes of me;
You are a spook of high degree."
"My good man," cried J. Wentworth B.,
"Leave me a little while, I pray,
I've traveled very far today,
And I desire to be alone
With him who sleeps beneath this stone.
I cannot rest till I have seen
My ancestor, Sir Godfrey Beane."

"Your ancestor! How can that be,"
Exclaimed the little ghost, "when he,
Last of his line, was drowned at sea
Two hundred years ago? This stone
Is to his memory alone.
I, and I only, saw his end.
As he, my master and my friend,
Leaned o'er the vessel's side one night
I pushed him—no, it was not right,
I own that I was much to blame;
I donned his clothes, and took the name
Of Beane—I also took his gold,
About five thousand pounds all told;
And so to Boston, Mass., I came
To found a family and name—
I, who in former times had been
Sir Godfrey's—"

                    "Wretch, what do you mean!
Sir Godfrey's what?" gasped Wentworth Beane.
"Sir Godfrey's valet!"

                    That same night,
When the ghost steamer sailed, you might

Among the passengers have seen
A ghost of very abject mien,
Faded and shrunk, forlorn and frayed,
The shadow of his former shade,
Who registered in steerage class,
J. W. Beane of Boston, Mass.

Now, gentle reader, do not try
To guess the family which I
Disguise as Beane—enough that they
Exist on Beacon Hill today,
In sweet enjoyment of their claims—
It is not well to mention names.

OLIVER HERFORD

Locked In

All my life I lived in a coconut.
It was cramped and dark.
Especially in the morning when I had to shave.
But what pained me most was that I had no way
to get into touch with the outside world.
If no one out there happened to find the coconut,
if no one cracked it, then I was doomed
to live all my life in the nut, and maybe even die there.
I died in the coconut.
A couple of years later they found the coconut,
cracked it, and found me shrunk and crumpled inside.
"What an accident!"
"If only we had found it earlier . . ."
"Then maybe we could have saved him."
"Maybe there are more of them locked in like that . . ."
"Whom we might be able to save,"

they said, and started knocking to pieces every coconut
within reach.

No use! Meaningless! A waste of time!
A person who chooses to live in a coconut!
Such a nut is one in a million!

But I have a brother-in-law who
lives in an
acorn.

INGEMAR GUSTAFSON
(Translated from the Swedish by MAY SWENSON)

Jean Richepin's Song

A poor lad once and a lad so trim,
  (Fol de rol de raly O!
    Fol de rol!)
A poor lad once and a lad so trim
Gave his love to her that loved not him.

And, says she, "Fetch me tonight, you rogue,"
  (Fol de rol de raly O!
    Fol de rol!)
And, says she, "Fetch me tonight, you rogue,
Your mother's heart to feed my dog!"

To his mother's house went that young man,
  (Fol de rol de raly O!
    Fol de rol!)
To his mother's house went that young man,
Killed her, and took the heart, and ran.

And as he was running, look you, he fell,
  (Fol de rol de raly O!
    Fol de rol!)
And as he was running, look you, he fell,
And the heart rolled on the ground as well.

And the lad, as the heart was a-rolling, heard,
  (*Fol de rol de raly, O!*
     Fol de rol!)
And the lad, as the heart was a-rolling, heard
That the heart was speaking, and this was the word—

The heart was a-weeping, and crying so small,
  (*Fol de rol de raly O!*
     Fol de rol!)
The heart was a-weeping and crying so small,
"Are you hurt, my child, are you hurt at all?"

HERBERT TRENCH

Screaming Tarn

The saddest place that e'er I saw
  Is the deep tarn above the inn
That crowns the mountain road, whereby
  One southward bound his way must win.

Sunk on the table of the ridge
  From its deep shores is naught to see:
The unresting wind lashes and chills
  Its shivering ripples ceaselessly.

Three sides 'tis banked with stones aslant,
  And down the fourth the rushes grow,
And yellow sedge fringing the edge
  With lengthen'd image all arow.

'Tis square and black, and on its face
  When noon is still, the mirror'd sky
Looks dark and further from the earth
  Than when you gaze at it on high.

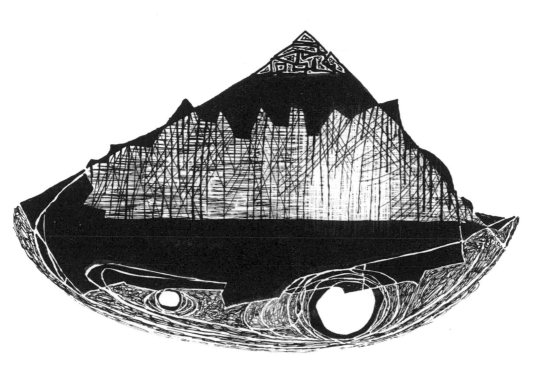

At mid of night, if one be there
  —So say the people of the hill—
A fearful shriek of death is heard,
  One sudden scream both loud and shrill.

And some have seen on stilly nights,
  And when the moon was clear and round,
Bubbles which to the surface swam
  And burst as if they held the sound.—

'Twas in the days ere hapless Charles
  Losing his crown had lost his head,
This tale is told of him who kept
  The inn upon the watershed:

He was a lowbred ruin'd man
   Whom lawless times set free from fear:
One evening to his house there rode
   A young and gentle cavalier.

With curling hair and linen fair
   And jewel-hilted sword he went;
The horse he rode he had ridden far,
   And he was with his journey spent.

He asked a lodging for the night,
   His valise from his steed unbound,
He let none bear it but himself
   And set it by him on the ground.

"Here's gold or jewels," thought the host,
   "That's carrying south to find the king."
He chattered many a loyal word,
   And scraps of royal airs 'gan sing.

His guest thereat grew more at ease
   And o'er his wine he gave a toast,
But little ate, and to his room
   Carried his sack behind the host.

"Now rest you well," the host he said,
   But of his wish the word fell wide;
Nor did he now forget his son
   Who fell in fight by Cromwell's side.

Revenge and poverty have brought
   Full gentler heart than his to crime;
And he was one by nature rude,
   Born to foul deeds at any time.

With unshod feet at dead of night
   In stealth he to the guest room crept,

Lantern and dagger in his hand,
    And stabbed his victim while he slept.

But as he struck a scream there came,
    A fearful scream so loud and shrill:
He whelm'd the face with pillows o'er,
    And lean'd till all had long been still.

Then to the face the flame he held
    To see there should no life remain:—
When lo! his brutal heart was quell'd:
    'Twas a fair woman he had slain.

The tan upon her face was paint,
    The manly hair was torn away,
Soft was the breast that he had pierced;
    Beautiful in her death she lay.

His was no heart to faint at crime,
    Tho' half he wished the deed undone.
He pulled the valise from the bed
    To find what booty he had won.

He cut the straps, and pushed within
    His murderous fingers to their theft.
A deathly sweat came o'er his brow,
    He had no sense nor meaning left.

He touched not gold, it was not cold,
    It was not hard, it felt like flesh.
He drew out by the curling hair
    A young man's head, and murder'd fresh;

A young man's head, cut by the neck.
    But what was dreader still to see,
Her whom he had slain he saw again,
    The twain were like as like can be.

Brother and sister if they were,
    Both in one shroud they now were wound,—
Across his back and down the stair,
    Out of the house without a sound.

He made his way unto the tarn,
    The night was dark and still and dank;
The ripple chuckling 'neath the boat
    Laughed as he drew it to the bank.

Upon the bottom of the boat
    He laid his burden flat and low,
And on them laid the square sandstones
    That round about the margin go.

Stone upon stone he weighed them down,
    Until the boat would hold no more;
The freeboard now was scarce an inch:
    He stripp'd his clothes and push'd from shore.

All naked to the middle pool
    He swam behind in the dark night;
And there he let the water in
    And sank his terror out of sight.

He swam ashore, and donn'd his dress,
    And scraped his bloody fingers clean;
Ran home and on his victim's steed
    Mounted, and never more was seen.

But to a comrade ere he died
    He told his story guess'd of none:
So from his lips the crime returned
    To haunt the spot where it was done.

ROBERT BRIDGES

The Tale the Hermit Told

It was one afternoon when I was young
in a village near here, which no one now remembers—
why, I will tell you—an afternoon of fiesta,
with the bells of the hermitage echoing in the mountains,
and a buzz of voices, and dogs barking. Some said
it could all be heard as far as Calatayud.
I was a boy then, though at that perilous point
when tiny things could terrify and amaze me.
The dust in the village square had been watered down,
and we waited, laughing and jostling
the satin rumps of the gipsy dancers.
Across from us, the girls, all lace and frills,
fluttered like tissue paper. Then at a signal,
as the charcoal-burner's dog rolled over and over,
shedding its ribbons, the village band
blundered into tune, and the day began.
    The dancing dizzied me. There was one gipsy
unlike the others, tall, who spun on her feet,
laughing to herself, lost in her own amazement.
I watched her as though in a dream. All round,
my uncles and other men were calling *olé*
while the women tittered and pouted.
There were more feet than shoes, more wine than glasses,
and more kisses than lips. The sun was burning.
Next came a magician, an ugly sly-eyed man
not from our district. "Fiesta, fiesta" he called,
then, chanting a kind of spell, he swore
he would conjure a live dove out of the air.
I saw the dove's wing peeping from his pocket,
so I wandered away, hating the sound of him,
among the tables, heavy with food and wine.
And there was the gipsy girl, standing alone,
head turned away to listen, as though she heard

bells in the hills. She saw me, and her eyes,
which were azure, not black, mocked me.
I could not stop looking. Lightly she danced across
and, keeping her eyes on mine, poured out
a glass of golden wine, and put it before me.

I glanced from her eyes to the wine. In it, the sun
was a small gold coin, the people looked like nuts.
The band were brass buttons, the towering mountains
the size of pebbles, the houses, matchboxes
about the thumbnail square. A miniature magician
was letting loose a dove, which floated upwards,
and there, in the golden, glass-held afternoon,
were those mocking eyes. Time in that moment hung
upside down. In a gulp, I drank the wine.

What happened next? You must listen.
Goggling boys, girls, dogs, band, gipsies, village,
dove, magician, all rolled down my throat.
Even the music glugged once and was gone.
I was standing nowhere, horrified, alone,
waiting for her eyes to appear and laugh
the afternoon back, but nothing moved or happened.
Nothing, nothing, nothing.

All that night, I lay in a clump of pines
and seemed to hear the hunters with their dogs
(unribboned now) closing to flush me out.
I hid my face in the needles. All the next day,
I tried to wish the village back, to vomit
the wine, to free the white dove and the music.
I could not. And as time passed,
I lived on bitter nuts and bark and grasses,
and grew used to the woods. I am still here
on this barren mountainside. The years are nothing.

Yet I am sure of this—
that somewhere in my body there is fiesta,
with ribboned dogs, balloons, and children dancing
in a lost village, that only I remember.
Often I have visions, and I hear

voices I know call out. Was it the false magician
who tempted me to magic? Or was it
the gipsy girl who dropped her eyes in a glass
and asked me to work wonders?
Even now, in age, I wait to see her,
still a girl, come spiraling through the woods,
bringing her mystery to me, and with her eyes
teaching me to undream myself, and be
a boy again, believing in a dove
made out of air, that circles overhead
on a lost afternoon of fiesta.

ALASTAIR REID

The Feckless Dinner Party

"Who are we waiting for?" "*Soup* burnt?" . . . Eight.
  "Only the tiniest party!—Us!"
"Darling! Divine!" "Ten minutes late—"
  "And my digest—" "I'm *ravenous!*"
  " 'Toomes'?"—Oh, he's new." "Looks crazed, I guess!"
  " 'Married'—*Again!*" "Well; more or less!"

"Dinner is *served!*" " 'Dinner is served.' "
  "Is served?" "Is served." "Ah, yes."

"Dear Mr. Prout, will you take down
  The Lilith in leaf-green by the fire?
Blanche Ogleton? . . ." "How coy a frown!—
  Hasn't she borrowed *Eve's* attire?"
"Morose Old Adam!" "Charmed—I vow."
  "Come then, and meet her now."

"Now, Dr. Mallus—would you please?—
  Our daring poetess, Delia Seek?"
"The lady with the bony knees?"

[33]

"And—*entre nous*—less song than beak."
"Sharing her past with Simple Si—"
   "*Bare* facts! He'll blush!" "Oh, fie!"

"And *you,* Sir Nathan—false but fair!—
   That fountain of wit, Aurora Pert."
"More wit than It, poor dear! But there . . ."
   "Pitiless Pacha! *And* such a flirt!"
" 'Flirt'! *Me?*" "Who else?" "You here. . . . Who can . . . ?"
   "In*corr*igible man!"

"And now, Mr. Simon—little me!—
   Last and—" "By no means least!" "Oh, come!—
What naughty, naughty flattery!
   Honey!—I hear the creature hum!"
"Sweets for the sweet, *I* always say!"
   " 'Always'? . . . We're last." "*This* way?" . . .

"No, sir; straight on, please." "I'd have vowed!—
   I came the other . . ." "It's queer; I'm sure . . ."
"What frightful pictures!" "Fiends!" "The *crowd!*"
   "Such nudes!" "I can't endure . . ."

"Yes, *there* they go." "Heavens! *Are* we right?"
   "Follow up closer!" " 'Prout'?—sand-blind!"
"This endless . . ." "Who's turned down the light?"
   "Keep calm! They're close behind."

"Oh! Dr. Mallus; what dismal stairs!"
   "I hate these old Victor . . ." "Dry rot!"
"Darker and darker!" "Fog!" "The air's . . ."
   "Scarce breathable!" "Hell!" "*What?*"

"The banister's gone!" "It's deep; keep close!"
   "We're going down and down!" "What fun!"
"Damp! Why, my shoes . . ." "It's slimy . . . Not *moss!*"
   "I'm freezing cold!" "Let's run."

"... Behind us. I'm giddy. ..." "The catacombs ..."
  "That shout!" "Who's there?" "I'm *alone!*" "Stand back!"
"She said, Lead ..." "Oh!" "Where's Toomes?" *"Toomes!"*
    "Toomes!"
  "Stifling!" "My skull will crack!"

"Sir Nathan! *Ai!*" "I *say! Toomes!* Prout!"
  "Where? Where?" " 'Our silks and fine array' ..."
"She's mad." "I'm dying!" "Oh, let me *out!*"
  "My God! We've lost our way!" ...

And now how sad-serene the abandoned house,
Whereon at dawn the spring-tide sunbeams beat;
And time's slow pace alone is ominous,
And naught but shadows of noonday therein meet;
Domestic microcosm, only a Trump could rouse:
And, pondering darkly, in the silent rooms,
He who misled them all—the butler, Toomes.

WALTER DE LA MARE

Mary's Ghost

'Twas in the middle of the night,
  To sleep young William tried,
When Mary's ghost came stealing in,
  And stood at his bedside.

O William dear! O William dear!
  My rest eternal ceases;
Alas! my everlasting peace
  Is broken into pieces.

I thought the last of all my cares
  Would end with my last minute;

But tho' I went to my long home,
  I didn't stay long in it.

The body-snatchers they have come,
  And made a snatch at me;
It's very hard them kind of men
  Won't let a body be!

You thought that I was buried deep,
  Quite decent like and chary,
But from her grave in Mary-bone
  They've come and boned your Mary.

The arm that used to take your arm
  Is took to Dr. Vyse;
And both my legs are gone to walk
  The hospital at Guy's.

I vowed that you should have my hand,
  But fate gives us denial;
You'll find it there, at Dr. Bell's,
  In spirits and a phial.

As for my feet, the little feet
  You used to call so pretty,
There's one, I know, in Bedford Row,
  The t'other's in the City.

I can't tell where my head is gone,
  But Dr. Carpue can;
As for my trunk, it's all packed up
  To go by Pickford's van.

I wish you'd go to Mr. P.
  And save me such a ride;
I don't half like the outside place,
  They've took for my inside.

The cock it crows—I must be gone!
    My William, we must part!
But I'll be yours in death, although
    Sir Astley has my heart.

Don't go to weep upon my grave,
    And think that there I be;
They haven't left an atom there
    Of my anatomie.

THOMAS HOOD

Bedtime Story

Long long ago when the world was a wild place
Planted with bushes and peopled by apes, our
Mission Brigade was at work in the jungle.
    Hard by the Congo

Once, when a foraging detail was active
Scouting for green-fly, it came on a gray man, the
Last living man, in the branch of a baobab
    Stalking a monkey.

Earlier men had disposed of, for pleasure,
Creatures whose names we scarcely remember—
Zebra, rhinoceros, elephants, warthog,
    Lion, rats, deer. But

After the wars had extinguished the cities
Only the wild ones were left, half-naked
Near the Equator: and here was the last one,
    Starved for a monkey.

By then the Mission Brigade had encountered
Hundreds of such men: and their procedure,

[37]

History tells us, was only to feed them:
    Find them and feed them;

Those were the orders. And this was the last one.
Nobody knew that he was, but he was. Mud
Caked on his flat gray flanks. He was crouched, half-armed with
    a shaved spear

Glinting beneath broad leaves. When their jaws cut
Swathes through the bark and he saw fine teeth shine,
Round eyes roll round and forked arms waver
    Huge as the rough trunks

Over his head, he was frightened. Our workers
Marched through the Congo before he was born, but
This was the first time perhaps that he'd seen one.
    Staring in hot still

Silence, he crouched there: then jumped. With a long swing
Down from his branch, he had angled his spear too
Quickly, before they could hold him, and hurled it
    Hard at the soldier

Leading the detail. How could he know Queen's
Orders were only to help him? The soldier
Winced when the tipped spear pricked him. Unsheathing his
    Sting was a reflex.

Later the Queen was informed. There were no more
Men. An impetuous soldier had killed off,
Purely by chance, the penultimate primate.
    When she was certain,

Squadrons of workers were fanned through the Congo
Detailed to bring back the man's picked bones to be
Sealed in the archives in amber. I'm quite sure
    Nobody found them

After the most industrious search, though.
Where had the bones gone? Over the earth, dear,
Ground by the teeth of the termites, blown by the
     Wind, like the dodo's.

GEORGE MACBETH

A Lady Comes to an Inn

Three strange men came to the Inn.
One was a black man, pocked and thin,
One was brown with a silver knife,
And one brought with him a beautiful wife.

That lovely woman had hair as pale
As French champagne or finest ale,
That lovely woman was long and slim
As a young white birch or a maple limb.

Her face was like cream, her mouth was a rose,
What language she spoke nobody knows,
But sometimes she'd scream like a cockatoo
And swear wonderful oaths that nobody knew.

Her great silk skirts like a silver bell
Down to her little bronze slippers fell,
And her low-cut gown showed a dove on its nest
In blue tattooing across her breast.

Nobody learned the lady's name,
Nor the marvelous land from which they came,
But still they tell through the countryside
The tale of those men and that beautiful bride.

ELIZABETH J. COATSWORTH

The Beetle in the Wood

"Because the beetle that lives in the wood
Is *knock-knock-knocking* aloud, I fear
Some ill is afoot in the neighborhood.
Death-knock of the beetle I hear.

"I wonder who it is going to die?
Girl's or granny's the fearful fate?
Nobody here in the house but I,
Nobody here but my lone . . . but wait . . .

"Last night betwixt two lids of sleep,
And all in the drowsing house grown still,

I heard the sound of something acreep
Over the windowsill,

"And what was that sound as I swept the soot
From the whitewashed hearth I had scoured with care,
That sound as of a fumbling foot
Stepping now here, now there?

"When night like a black cat comes to sneak
Up the stairs, I think too much . . .
What was that brushing against my cheek
With a stealthy moth-wing touch!

"No rest tonight though my best geese gave
Their breasts to pluck for my pillow of down.
It's quiet, quiet almost as the grave . . .
Now I hear the screech owl's sound,

"And all my bones are atingle with dread,
And midnight passes, and one o'clock,
And the beetle still in the wood of the bed
Is *knock-knock-knocking* . . .
             is *knock-knock-knock* . . ."

                                   BYRON HERBERT REECE

Eve

Eve, with her basket was
Deep in the bells and grass,
Wading in bells and grass
Up to her knees,
Picking a dish of sweet
Berries and plums to eat,
Down in the bells and grass
Under the trees.

Mute as a mouse in a

Corner the cobra lay,
Curled round a bough of the
Cinnamon tall. . . .
Now to get even and
Humble proud heaven and—
Now was the moment or
Never at all.

"Eva!" Each syllable
Light as a flower fell,
"Eva!" he whispered the
Wondering maid,
Soft as a bubble sung
Out of a linnet's lung,
Soft and most silverly
"Eva!" he said.

Picture that orchard sprite,
Eve, with her body white,
Supple and smooth to her
Slim fingertips,
Wondering, listening,
Listening, wondering,
Eve with a berry
Halfway to her lips.

Oh, had our simple Eve
Seen through the make-believe!
Had she but known the
Pretender he was!
Out of the boughs he came,
Whispering still her name,
Tumbling in twenty rings
Into the grass.

Here was the strangest pair
In the world anywhere,
Eve in the bells and grass

Kneeling, and he
Telling his story low. . . .
Singing birds saw them go
Down the dark path to
The Blasphemous Tree.

Oh, what a clatter when
Titmouse and Jenny Wren
Saw him successful and
Taking his leave!
How the birds rated him!
How they all hated him!
How they all pitied
Poor motherless Eve!

Picture her crying
Outside in the lane,
Eve, with no dish of sweet
Berries and plums to eat,
Haunting the gate of the
Orchard in vain. . . .
Picture the lewd delight
Under the hill tonight—
"Eva!" the toast goes round,
"Eva!" again.

RALPH HODGSON

A Smuggler's Song

If you wake at midnight, and hear a horse's feet,
Don't go drawing back the blind, or looking in the street.
Them that ask no questions isn't told a lie.
Watch the wall, my darling, while the Gentlemen go by!
          Five and twenty ponies,
          Trotting through the dark—

Brandy for the parson,
'Baccy for the clerk;
Laces for a lady, letters for a spy,
And watch the wall, my darling, while the Gentlemen go by!

Running round the woodlump if you chance to find
Little barrels, roped and tarred, all full of brandy-wine,
Don't you shout to come and look, nor use 'em for your play.
Put the brushwood back again—and they'll be gone next day!

If you see the stable door setting open wide;
If you see a tired horse lying down inside;
If your mother mends a coat cut about and tore;
If the lining's wet and warm—don't you ask no more!

If you meet King George's men, dressed in blue and red,
You be careful what you say, and mindful what is said.
If they call you "pretty maid," and chuck you 'neath the chin,
Don't you tell where no one is, nor yet where no one's been!

Knocks and footsteps round the house—whistles after dark—
You've no call for running out till the house dogs bark.
Trusty's here, and Pincher's here, and see how dumb they lie—
They don't fret to follow when the Gentlemen go by!

If you do as you've been told, likely there's a chance
You'll be give a dainty doll, all the way from France,
With a cap of Valenciennes, and a velvet hood—
A present from the Gentlemen, along o' being good!
Five and twenty ponies,
Trotting through the dark—
Brandy for the parson,
'Baccy for the clerk.
Them that asks no questions isn't told a lie—
Watch the wall, my darling, while the Gentlemen go by!

RUDYARD KIPLING

And in the Hanging Gardens

And in the hanging gardens there is rain
From midnight until one, striking the leaves
And bells of flowers, and stroking boles of planes,
And drawing slow arpeggios over pools
And stretching strings of sound from eaves to ferns.
The princess reads. The knave of diamonds sleeps.
The king is drunk, and flings a golden goblet
Down from the turret window (curtained with rain)
Into the lilacs.

          And at one o'clock
The vulcan under the garden wakes and beats
The gong upon his anvil. Then the rain
Ceases, but gently ceases, dripping still,
And sound of falling water fills the dark
As leaves grow bold and upright, and as eaves
Part with water. The princess turns the page
Beside the candle, and between two braids
Of golden hair. And reads: "From there I went
Northward a journey of four days, and came
To a wild village in the hills, where none
Was living save the vulture and the rat
And one old man who laughed but could not speak.
The roofs were fallen in, the well grown over
With weeds. And it was here my father died.
Then eight days further, bearing slightly west,
The cold wind blowing sand against our faces,
The food tasting of sand. And as we stood
By the dry rock that marks the highest point
My brother said: 'Not too late is it yet
To turn, remembering home.' And we were silent
Thinking of home." The princess shuts her eyes
And feels the tears forming beneath her eyelids
And opens them, and tears fall on the page.

The knave of diamonds in the darkened room
Throws off his covers, sleeps, and snores again.
The king goes slowly down the turret stairs
To find the goblet.

    And at two o'clock
The vulcan in his smithy underground
Under the hanging gardens, where the drip
Of rain among the clematis and ivy
Still falls from sipping flower to purple flower,
Smites twice his anvil, and murmur comes
Among the roots and vines. The princess reads,
"As I am sick, and cannot write you more,
And have not long to live, I give this letter
To him, my brother, who will bear it south
And tell you how I died. Ask how it was,
There in the northern desert, where the grass
Was withered, and the horses, all but one,
Perished . . ." The princess drops her golden head
Upon the page between her two white arms
And golden braids. The knave of diamonds wakes
And at his window in the darkened room
Watches the lilacs tossing, where the king
Seeks for the goblet.

    And at three o'clock
The moon inflames the lilac heads, and thrice
The vulcan, in his root-bound smithy, clangs
His anvil; and the sounds creep softly up
Among the vines and walls. The moon is round,
Round as a shield above the turret top.
The princess blows her candle out, and weeps
In the pale room, where scent of lilacs comes,
Weeping, with hands across her eyelids, thinking
Of withered grass, withered by sandy wind.
The knave of diamonds, in his darkened room,

Holds in his hands a key, and softly steps
Along the corridor, and slides the key
Into the door that guards her. Meanwhile, slowly,
The king, with raindrops on his beard and hands,
And dripping sleeves, climbs up the turret stairs,
Holding the goblet upright in one hand;
And pauses on the midmost step, to taste
One drop of wine, wherewith wild rain has mixed.

CONRAD AIKEN

The Green Gnome

Ring, sing! ring, sing! pleasant Sabbath bells!
Chime, rhyme! chime, rhyme! through dales and dells!
Rhyme, ring! chime, sing! pleasant Sabbath bells!
Chime, sing! rhyme, ring! over fields and fells!

And I galloped and I galloped on my palfrey white as milk,
My robe was of the sea-green woof, my serk was of the silk;
My hair was golden-yellow, and it floated to my shoe,
My eyes were like two harebells bathed in little drops of dew;
My palfrey, never stopping, made a music sweetly blent
With the leaves of autumn dropping all around me as I went;
And I heard the bells, grown fainter, far behind me peal and play,
Fainter, fainter, fainter, till they seemed to die away;
And beside a silver runnel, on a little heap of sand,
I saw the green gnome sitting, with his cheek upon his hand.
Then he started up to see me, and he ran with a cry and bound,
And drew me from my palfrey white and set me on the ground.
O crimson, crimson were his locks, his face was green to see,
But he cried, "O light-haired lassie, you are bound to marry me!"
He clasped me round the middle small, he kissed me on the cheek,
He kissed me once, he kissed me twice—I could not stir or speak;

He kissed me twice, he kissed me thrice; but when he kissed again,
I called aloud upon the name of Him who died for men.

Sing, sing! ring, ring! pleasant Sabbath bells!
Chime, rhyme! chime, rhyme! through dales and dells!
Rhyme, ring! chime, sing! pleasant Sabbath bells!
Chime, sing! rhyme, ring! over fields and fells!

O faintly, faintly, faintly, calling men and maids to pray,
So faintly, faintly, faintly rang the bells afar away;
And as I named the Blessed Name, as in our need we can,
The ugly green gnome became a tall and comely man:
His hands were white, his beard was gold, his eyes were black as
    sloes,
His tunic was of scarlet woof, and silken were his hose;
A pensive light from Faëryland still lingered on his cheek,
His voice was like the running brook when he began to speak:
"O, you have cast away the charm my step-dame put on me,
Seven years have I dwelt in Faëryland, and you have set me free.
O, I will mount thy palfrey white, and ride to kirk with thee,
And, by those dewy little eyes, we twain will wedded be!"

Back we galloped, never stopping, he before and I behind,
And the autumn leaves were dropping, red and yellow in the
    wind;
And the sun was shining clearer, and my heart was high and
    proud,
As nearer, nearer rang the kirkbells sweet and loud,
And we saw the kirk, before us, as we trotted down the fells,
And near, clearer, o'er us, rang the welcome of the bells.

Ring, sing! ring, sing! pleasant Sabbath bells!
Chime, rhyme! chime, rhyme! through dales and dells!
Rhyme, ring! chime, sing! pleasant Sabbath bells!
Chime, sing! rhyme, ring! over fields and fells!

ROBERT BUCHANAN

[48]

The Ballad of Minepit Shaw

About the time that taverns shut
    And men can buy no beer,
Two lads went up to the keeper's hut
    To steal Lord Pelham's deer.

Night and the liquor was in their heads—
    They laughed and talked no bounds,
Till they waked the keepers on their beds
And the keepers loosed the hounds.

They had killed a hart, they had killed a hind,
    Ready to carry away,
When they heard a whimper down the wind
    And they heard a bloodhound bay.

They took and ran across the fern,
    Their crossbows in their hand,
Till they met a man with a green lantern
    That called and bade 'em stand.

"What are ye doing, O Flesh and Blood,
    And what's your foolish will,
That you must break into Minepit Wood
    And wake the Folk of the Hill?"

"Oh, we've broke into Lord Pelham's park,
    And killed Lord Pelham's deer,
And if ever you heard a little dog bark
    You'll know why we come here.

"We ask you let us go our way,
    As fast as we can flee,
For if ever you heard a bloodhound bay
    You'll know how pressed we be."

"Oh, lay your crossbows on the bank
    And drop the knife from your hand,
And though the hounds are at your flank
    I'll save you where you stand!"

They laid their crossbows on the bank,
    They threw their knives in the wood,
And the ground before them opened and sank
    And saved 'em where they stood.

"Oh, what's the roaring in our ears
    That strikes us well-nigh dumb?"
"Oh, that is just how things appears
    According as they come."

"What are the stars before our eyes
    That strike us well-nigh blind?"
"Oh, that is just how things arise
    According as you find."

"And why's our bed so hard to the bones
    Excepting where it's cold?"
"Oh, that's because it is precious stones
    Excepting where 'tis gold.

"Think it over as you stand,
    For I tell you without fail,
If you haven't got into Fairyland
    You're not in Lewes Gaol."

All night long they thought of it,
    And, come the dawn, they saw
They'd tumbled into a great old pit,
    At the bottom of Minepit Shaw.

And the keeper's hound had followed 'em close,
    And broke her neck in the fall;

So they picked up their knives and their crossbows
   And buried the dog. That's all.

But whether the man was a poacher too
   Or a Pharisee so bold—
I reckon there's more things told than are true,
   And more things true than are told!

RUDYARD KIPLING

True Thomas

True Thomas lay on Huntlie bank;
   A marvel he did see;
For there he saw a lady bright
   Come riding down by the Eildon tree.

Her skirt was of grass-green silk,
   Her mantle of the velvet fine;
On every lock of her horse's mane
   Hung fifty silver bells and nine.

True Thomas he pulled off his cap,
   And bowed low down on his knee;
"Hail to thee, Mary, Queen of Heaven!
   For thy peer on earth could never be."

"O no, O no, Thomas," she said,
   "That name does not belong to me;
I'm but the Queen of fair Elfland,
   That am hither come to visit thee.

"Harp and carp, Thomas," she said,
   "Harp and carp along with me;

And if ye dare to kiss my lips,
    Sure of your body I will be."

"Betide me weal, betide me woe,
    That threat shall never frighten me!"
Then he has kissed her rosy lips,
    All underneath the Eildon tree.

"Now ye must go with me," she said,
    "True Thomas, ye must go with me;
And ye must serve me seven years,
    Through weal or woe as may chance to be."

She's mounted on her milk-white steed,
    She's taken True Thomas up behind;
And aye, whene'er her bridle rang,
    The steed flew swifter than the wind.

O they rode on, and farther on,
    The steed flew swifter than the wind;
Until they reached a desert wide,
    And living land was left behind.

"Light down, light down now, Thomas," she said,
    "And lean your head upon my knee;
Light down, and rest a little space,
    And I will show you marvels three.

"O see ye not yon narrow road,
    So thick beset with thorns and briers?
That is the path of righteousness,
    Though after it but few enquires.

"And see ye not yon broad, broad road,
    That stretches o'er the lily leven?
That is the path of wickedness,
    Though some call it the road to heaven.

"And see ye not yon bonny road,
   That winds about the green hillside?
That is the way to fair Elfland,
   Where you and I this night must bide.

"But, Thomas, ye shall hold your tongue,
   Whatever ye may hear or see;
For if ye speak word in Elfin land,
   Ye'll ne'er win back to your own countree!"

O they rode on, and farther on;
   They waded through rivers above the knee,
And they saw neither sun nor moon,
   But they heard the roaring of the sea.

 It was mirk, mirk night; there was no starlight;
   They waded through red blood to the knee;
For all the blood that's shed on the earth
   Runs through the springs o' that countree.

At last they came to a garden green,
   And she pulled an apple from a tree—
"Take this for thy wages, True Thomas;
   It will give thee the tongue that can never lie!"

"My tongue is my own," True Thomas he said,
   "A goodly gift ye would give to me!
I neither could to buy or sell
   At fair or tryst where I may be.

"I could neither speak to prince or peer,
   Nor ask of grace from fair ladye."
"Now hold thy peace!" the lady said,
   "For as I say, so must it be."

He has gotten a coat of the even cloth,
   And a pair of shoes of the velvet green;

And till seven years were gone and past,
    True Thomas on earth was never seen.

OLD SCOTTISH BALLAD

Green Broom

There was an old man lived out in the wood,
    His trade was a-cutting of broom, green broom;
He had but one son without thrift, without good,
    Who lay in his bed till 'twas noon, bright noon.

The old man awoke one morning and spoke,
    He swore he would fire the room, that room,
If his John would not rise and open his eyes,
    And away to the wood to cut broom, green broom.

So Johnny arose, and he slipped on his clothes,
    And away to the wood to cut broom, green broom,
He sharpened his knives, for once he contrives
    To cut a great bundle of broom, green broom.

When Johnny passed under a lady's fine house,
    Passed under a lady's fine room, fine room,
She called to her maid, "Go fetch me," she said,
    "Go fetch me the boy that sells broom, green broom."

When Johnny came into the lady's fine house,
    And stood in the lady's fine room, fine room;
"Young Johnny," she said, "will you give up your trade,
    And marry a lady in bloom, full bloom?"

Johnny gave his consent, and to church they both went,
    And he wedded the lady in bloom, full bloom,
At market and fair, all folks do declare,
    There is none like the boy that sold broom, green broom.

ANONYMOUS

Molly Means

Old Molly Means was a hag and a witch;
Chile of the devil, the dark, and sitch.
Her heavy hair hung thick in ropes
And her blazing eyes was black as pitch.
Imp at three and wench at 'leben
She counted her husbands to the number seben.
     O Molly, Molly, Molly Means
     There goes the ghost of Molly Means.

Some say she was born with a veil on her face
So she could look through unnatchal space
Through the future and through the past
And charm a body or an evil place
And every man could well despise
The evil look in her coal black eyes.
     Old Molly, Molly, Molly Means
     Dark is the ghost of Molly Means.

And when the tale begun to spread
Of evil and of holy dread:
Her black-hand arts and her evil powers
How she cast her spells and called the dead,
The younguns was afraid at night
And the farmers feared their crops would blight.
    Old Molly, Molly, Molly Means
    Cold is the ghost of Molly Means.

Then one dark day she put a spell
On a young gal-bride just come to dwell
In the lane just down from Molly's shack
And when her husband come riding back
His wife was barking like a dog
And on all fours like a common hog.
    O Molly, Molly, Molly Means
    Where is the ghost of Molly Means?

The neighbors come and they went away
And said she'd die before break of day
But her husband held her in his arms
And swore he'd break the wicked charms;
He'd search all up and down the land
And turn the spell on Molly's hand.
    O Molly, Molly, Molly Means
    Sharp is the ghost of Molly Means.

So he rode all day and he rode all night
And at the dawn he come in sight
Of a man who said he could move the spell
And cause the awful thing to dwell
On Molly Means, to bark and bleed
Till she died at the hands of her evil deed.
    Old Molly, Molly, Molly Means
    This is the ghost of Molly Means.

Sometimes at night through the shadowy trees
She rides along on a winter breeze.

You can hear her holler and whine and cry.
Her voice is thin and her moan is high,
And her cackling laugh or her barking cold
Bring terror to the young and old.
    O Molly, Molly, Molly Means
    Lean is the ghost of Molly Means.

MARGARET WALKER

The Princess and the Gypsies

As I looked out one May morning
    I saw the treetops green;
I said: "My crown I will lay down
    And live no more a queen."

Then I tripped down my golden steps
    Dressed in my silken gown,
And when I stood in the open wood
    I met some gypsies brown.

"O gentle, gentle gypsies
    That roam the wide world through,
Because I hate my crown and state,
    O let me come with you!

"My councillors are old and gray
    And sit in narrow chairs,
But you can hear the birds sing clear
    And your hearts are as light as theirs."

"If you would come along with us
    Then you must count the cost,
For though in Spring the sweet birds sing,
    In Winter comes the frost.

"Your ladies serve you all the day
    With courtesy and care,
Your fine-shod feet they tread so neat
    But a gypsy's feet go bare.

"You wash in water running warm
    Through basins all of gold;
The streams where we roam have silvery foam,
    But the streams, the streams are cold.

"And barley bread is bitter to taste,
    Whilst sugary cakes they please.
Which will you choose, O which will you choose,
    Which will you choose of these?

"For if you choose the mountain streams
    And barley bread to eat,
Your heart will be free as the birds in the tree
    But the stones will cut your feet.

"The mud will spoil your silken gown
    And stain your insteps high,
The dogs in the farm will wish you harm
    And bark as you go by.

"And though your heart grow deep and gay
    And your heart grow wise and rich,
The cold will make your bones to ache
    And you will die in a ditch."

"O gentle, gentle gypsies
    That roam the wide world through,
Although I praise your wandering ways
    I dare not come with you."

I hung about their fingers brown
    My ruby rings and chain,

And with my head as heavy as lead
    I turned me back again.

As I went up the palace steps
    I heard the gypsies laugh;
The birds of Spring so sweet did sing,
    My heart it broke in half.

FRANCES CORNFORD

The Enchanted Shirt

The King was sick. His cheek was red
    And his eye was clear and bright;
He ate and drank with a kingly zest,
    And peacefully snored at night.

But he said he was sick, and a king should know,
    And doctors came by the score.
They did not cure him. He cut off their heads
    And sent to the schools for more.

At last two famous doctors came,
    And one was as poor as a rat—
He had passed his life in studious toil,
    And never found time to grow fat.

The other had never looked in a book;
    His patients gave him no trouble:
If they recovered, they paid him well,
    If they died, their heirs paid double.

Together they looked at the royal tongue,
    As the King on his couch reclined;
In succession they thumped his august chest,
    But no trace of disease could find.

The old sage said, "You're as sound as a nut."
  "Hang him up," roared the King in a gale—
In a ten-knot gale of royal rage;
  The other leech grew a shade pale;

But he pensively rubbed his sagacious nose,
  And thus his prescription ran—
The King will be well if he sleeps one night
  In the Shirt of a Happy Man.

Wide o'er the realm the couriers rode,
  And fast their horses ran,
And many they saw, and to many they spoke,
  But they found no Happy Man.

They found poor men who would fain be rich,
  And rich who thought they were poor;
And men who twisted their waist in stays,
  And women that shorthose wore.

They saw two men by the roadside sit,
  And both bemoaned their lot;
For one had buried his wife, he said,
  And the other one had not.

At last they came to a village gate.
  A beggar lay whistling there;
He whistled, and sang, and laughed, and rolled
  On the grass in the soft June air.

The weary couriers paused and looked
  At the scamp so blithe and gay;
And one of them said, "Heaven save you, friend!
  You seem to be happy today."

"Oh yes, fair sirs," the rascal laughed,
  And his voice rang free and glad;

"An idle man has so much to do
    That he never has time to be sad."

"This is our man," the courier said;
    "Our luck has led us aright.
I will give you a hundred ducats, friend,
    For the loan of your shirt tonight."

The merry blackguard lay back on the grass,
    And laughed till his face was black;
"I would do it, God wot," and he roared with the fun,
    "But I haven't a shirt to my back."
    .   .   .   .

Each day to the King the reports came in
    Of his unsuccessful spies,
And the sad panorama of human woes
    Passed daily under his eyes.

And he grew ashamed of his useless life,
    And his maladies hatched in gloom;
He opened his windows and let the air
    Of the free heaven into his room.

And out he went in the world, and toiled
    In his own appointed way;
And the people blessed him, the land was glad,
    And the King was well and gay.

JOHN HAY

The Devil's Bag

I saw the Devil walking down the lane
Behind our house.—A heavy bag
Was strapped upon his shoulders and the rain
Sizzled when it hit him.

He picked a rag
Up from the ground and put it in his sack,
And grinned, and rubbed his hands.
There was a thing
Alive inside the bag upon his back
—It must have been a soul! I saw it fling
And twist about inside, and not a hole
Or cranny for escape! Oh, it was sad!
I cried, and shouted out—*Let out that soul!*
But he turned round, and, sure, his face went mad,
And twisted up and down, and he said *"Hell!"*
And ran away. . . . Oh, mammy, I'm not well!

JAMES STEPHENS

The Shepherd's Tale

FROM THE FRENCH OF RAOUL PONCHON

Woman, you'll never credit what
    My two eyes saw this night . . .
But first of all we'll have a drop,
    It's freezing now, all right.

Ah, this wine's the stuff, by Mary!
    When he's grown up a bit,
That little fellow, just you see,
    He shall have some of it!

We might have all been knelt there yet,
    Put a Yule log on the fire,
But suddenly he starts to fret—
    He'd begun to tire.

Then "Sirs," his mother she did say,
    "It grieves me to remind

You that it's time to go away
    When you have been so kind.

"But see, how sleepy he's become,
    He's crying, let him rest.
You all know how to find our home—
    Each one's a welcome guest."

And so in silence we went out,
    But the funniest thing—
Those three fine kings, so rich and stout,
    Did wish me good-morning!

You see, love, that's how it began.
    The God born on the earth
This night's no ordinary one.
    Let's celebrate his birth!

                              JAMES KIRKUP

My Aunt's Spectre

They tell me (but I really can't
    Imagine such a rum thing),
It is the phantom of my aunt,
    Who ran away—or something.

It is the very worst of bores:
    (My aunt was most delightful).
It prowls about the corridors,
    And utters noises frightful.

At midnight through the rooms It glides,
    Behaving very coolly,
Our hearts all throb against our sides—
    The lights are burning bluely.

The lady, in her living hours,
　　Was the most charming vixen
That ever this poor sex of ours
　　Delighted to play tricks on.

Yes, that's her portrait on the wall,
　　In quaint old-fangled bodice:
Her eyes are blue—her waist is small—
　　A ghost! Pooh, pooh—a goddess!

A fine patrician shape, to suit
　　My dear old father's sister—
Lips softly curved, a dainty foot:
　　Happy the man that kissed her!

Light hair of crisp irregular curl
　　Over fair shoulders scattered—
Egad, she was a pretty girl,
　　Unless Sir Thomas flattered!

And who the deuce, in these bright days,
　　Could possibly expect her
To take to dissipated ways,
　　And plague us as a spectre?

MORTIMER COLLINS

The Ballad of the Harp-Weaver

"Son," said my mother,
　　When I was knee-high,
"You've need of clothes to cover you,
　　And not a rag have I.

"There's nothing in the house
　　To make a boy breeches,

Nor shears to cut a cloth with
  Nor thread to take stitches.

"There's nothing in the house
  But a loaf-end of rye,
And a harp with a woman's head
  Nobody will buy,"
And she began to cry.

That was in the early fall.
  When came the late fall,
"Son," she said, "the sight of you
  Makes your mother's blood crawl—

"Little skinny shoulder blades
  Sticking through your clothes!
And where you'll get a jacket from
  God above knows.

"It's lucky for me, lad,
  Your daddy's in the ground,
And can't see the way I let
  His son go around!"
  And she made a queer sound.

That was in the late fall.
  When the winter came,
I'd not a pair of breeches
  Nor a shirt to my name.

I couldn't go to school,
  Or out of doors to play.
And all the other little boys
  Passed our way.

"Son," said my mother,
  "Come, climb into my lap,

And I'll chafe your little bones
    While you take a nap."

And, oh, but we were silly
    For half an hour or more,
Me with my long legs
    Dragging on the floor,

A-rock-rock-rocking
    To a Mother Goose rhyme!
Oh, but we were happy
    For half an hour's time!

But there was I, a great boy,
    And what would folks say
To hear my mother singing me
    To sleep all day,
    In such a daft way?

Men say the winter
    Was bad that year;
Fuel was scarce,
    And food was dear.

A wind with a wolf's head
    Howled about our door,
And we burned up the chairs
    And sat upon the floor.

All that was left us
    Was a chair we couldn't break,
And the harp with a woman's head
    Nobody would take,
    For song or pity's sake.

The night before Christmas
    I cried with the cold,

I cried myself to sleep
  Like a two-year-old.

And in the deep night
  I felt my mother rise,
And stare down upon me
  With love in her eyes.

I saw my mother sitting
  On the one good chair,
A light falling on her
  From I couldn't tell where,

Looking nineteen,
  And not a day older,
And the harp with a woman's head
  Leaned against her shoulder.

Her thin fingers, moving
  In the thin, tall strings,
Were weav-weav-weaving
  Wonderful things.

Many bright threads,
  From where I couldn't see,
Were running through the harp strings
  Rapidly,

And gold threads whistling
  Through my mother's hand.
I saw the web grow,
  And the pattern expand.

She wove a child's jacket,
  And when it was done
She laid it on the floor
  And wove another one.

She wove a red cloak
  So regal to see,
"She's made it for a king's son,"
  I said, "and not for me."
  But I knew it was for me.

She wove a pair of breeches
  Quicker that that!
She wove a pair of boots
  And a little cocked hat.

She wove a pair of mittens,
  She wove a little blouse,
She wove all night
  In the still, cold house.

She sang as she worked,
  And the harp strings spoke;
Her voice never faltered,
  And the thread never broke.
  And when I awoke—

There sat my mother
  With the harp against her shoulder,
Looking nineteen,
  And not a day older,

A smile about her lips,
  And a light about her head,
And her hands in the harp strings
  Frozen dead.

And piled up beside her
  And toppling to the skies,
Were the clothes of a king's son,
  Just my size.

EDNA ST. VINCENT MILLAY

The Watch

When I
took my
watch to the watchfixer I
felt privileged but also pained to watch the operation. He
had long fingernails and a voluntary squint. He
fixed a magnifying cup over his
squint eye. He
undressed my
watch. I
watched him
split her
in three layers and lay her
middle—a quivering viscera—in a circle on a little plinth. He
shoved shirt sleeves up and leaned like an ogre over my
naked watch. With critical pincers he
poked and stirred. He
lifted out little private things with a magnet too tiny for me
to watch almost. "Watch out!" I
almost said. His
eye watched, enlarged, the secrets of my
watch, and I
watched anxiously. Because what if he
touched her
ticker too rough, and she
gave up the ghost out of pure fright? Or put her
things back backwards so she'd
run backwards after this? Or he
might lose a minuscule part, connected to her
exquisite heart, and mix her
up, instead of fix her.
And all the time,
all the time-
pieces on the walls, on the shelves, told the time,
told the time

in swishes and ticks,
swishes and ticks,
and seemed to be gloating, as they watched and told. I
felt faint, I
was about to lose my
breath—my
ticker going lickety-split—when watchfixer clipped her
three slices together with a gleam and two flicks of his
tools like chopsticks. He
spat out his
eye, lifted her
high, gave her
a twist, set her
hands right, and laid her
little face, quite as usual, in its place on my
wrist.

MAY SWENSON

A Dream

I heard the dogs howl in the moonlight night;
I went to the window to see the sight;
All the Dead that ever I knew
Going one by one and two by two.

On they pass'd, and on they pass'd;
Townsfellows all, from first to last;
Born in the moonlight of the lane,
Quench'd in the heavy shadow again.

Schoolmates, marching as when we play'd
At soldiers once—but now more staid;
Those were the strangest sight to me
Who were drown'd, I knew, in the awful sea.

Straight and handsome folk; bent and weak too;
Some that I loved, and gasp'd to speak to;
Some but a day in their churchyard bed;
Some that I had not known were dead.

A long, long crowd—where each seem'd lonely,
Yet of them all there was one, one only,
Raised a head or look'd my way;
She linger'd a moment—she might not stay.

How long since I saw that fair pale face!
Ah! Mother dear! might I only place
My head on thy breast, a moment to rest,
While thy hand on my tearful cheek were prest.

On, on a moving bridge they made
Across the moon-stream from shade to shade,
Young and old, women and men;
Many long forgot, but remember'd then.

And first there came a bitter laughter;
A sound of tears the moment after;
And then a music so lofty and gay,
That every morning, day by day,
I strive to recall it if I may.

WILLIAM ALLINGHAM

Characters
and Individualists

Get Up and Bar the Door

It fell about the Martinmas time,
   And a gay time it was then,
When our goodwife got puddings to make,
   And she's boiled them in the pan.

The wind so cold blew south and north,
   And blew into the floor;
Quoth our goodman to our goodwife,
   "Get up and bar the door."

"My hand is in my household work,
   Goodman, as ye may see;
And it will not be barred for a hundred years,
   If it's to be barred by me!"

They made a pact between them both,
   They made it firm and sure,
That whosoe'er should speak the first,
   Should rise and bar the door.

Then by there came two gentlemen,
    At twelve o'clock at night,
And they could see neither house nor hall,
    Nor coal nor candlelight.

"Now whether is this a rich man's house,
    Or whether is it a poor?"
But never a word would one of them speak,
    For barring of the door.

The guests they ate the white puddings,
    And then they ate the black;
Tho' much the goodwife thought to herself,
    Yet never a word she spake.

Then said one stranger to the other,
    "Here, man, take ye my knife;
Do ye take off the old man's beard,
    And I'll kiss the goodwife."

"There's no hot water to scrape it off,
    And what shall we do then?"
"Then why not use the pudding broth,
    That boils into the pan?"

O up then started our goodman,
    An angry man was he;
"Will ye kiss my wife before my eyes!
    And with pudding broth scald me!"

Then up and started our goodwife,
    Gave three skips on the floor:
"Goodman, you've spoken the foremost word.
    Get up and bar the door!"

OLD BALLAD

Mr. Flood's Party

Old Eben Flood, climbing alone one night
Over the hill between the town below
And the forsaken upland hermitage
That held as much as he should ever know
On earth again of home, paused warily.
The road was his with not a native near;
And Eben, having leisure, said aloud,
For no man else in Tilbury Town to hear:

"Well, Mr. Flood, we have the harvest moon
Again, and we may not have many more;
The bird is on the wing, the poet says,
And you and I have said it here before.
Drink to the bird." He raised up to the light
The jug that he had gone so far to fill,
And answered huskily: "Well, Mr. Flood,
Since you propose it, I believe I will."

Alone, as if enduring to the end
A valiant armor of scarred hopes outworn,
He stood there in the middle of the road
Like Roland's ghost winding a silent horn.
Below him, in the town among the trees,
Where friends of other days had honored him,
A phantom salutation of the dead
Rang thinly till old Eben's eyes were dim.

Then, as a mother lays her sleeping child
Down tenderly, fearing it may awake,
He set the jug down slowly at his feet
With trembling care, knowing that most things break;
And only when assured that on firm earth
It stood, as the uncertain lives of men

Assuredly did not, he paced away,
And with his hand extended paused again:

"Well, Mr. Flood, we have not met like this
In a long time; and many a change has come
To both of us, I fear, since last it was
We had a drop together. Welcome home!"
Convivially returning with himself,
Again he raised the jug up to the light;
And with an acquiescent quaver said:
"Well, Mr. Flood, if you insist, I might.

"Only a very little, Mr. Flood—
For auld lang syne. No more, sir; that will do."
So, for the time, apparently it did,
And Eben evidently thought so too;
For soon amid the silver loneliness
Of night he lifted up his voice and sang,
Secure, with only two moons listening,
Until the whole harmonious landscape rang—

"For auld lang syne." The weary throat gave out,
The last word wavered, and the song was done.
He raised again the jug regretfully
And shook his head, and was again alone.
There was not much that was ahead of him,
And there was nothing in the town below—
Where strangers would have shut the many doors
That many friends had opened long ago.

EDWIN ARLINGTON ROBINSON

Bishop Hatto

The summer and autumn had been so wet
That in winter the corn was growing yet;

'Twas a piteous sight to see all around
The grain lie rotting on the ground.

Every day the starving poor
Crowded around Bishop Hatto's door,
For he had a plentiful last year's store,
And all the neighborhood could tell
His granaries were furnish'd well.

At last Bishop Hatto appointed a day
To quiet the poor without delay;
He bade them to his great barn repair,
And they should have food for the winter there.

Rejoiced such tidings good to hear,
The poor folk flock'd from far and near;
The great barn was full as it could hold
Of women and children, and young and old.

Then when he saw it could hold no more,
Bishop Hatto he made fast the door;
And while for mercy on Christ they call,
He set fire to the barn and burnt them all.

"I' faith, 'tis an excellent bonfire!" quoth he,
"And the country is greatly obliged to me,
For ridding it in these times forlorn
Of rats, that only consume the corn."

So then to his palace returned he,
And he sat down to supper merrily,
And he slept that night like an innocent man
But Bishop Hatto never slept again.

In the morning as he enter'd the hall,
Where his picture hung against the wall,
A sweat like death all over him came,
For the rats had eaten it out of the frame.

As he look'd there came a man from the farm,
He had a countenance white with alarm;
"My lord, I open'd your granaries this morn,
And the rats had eaten all your corn."

Another came running presently,
And he was pale as pale could be,
"Fly! my Lord Bishop, fly," quoth he,
"Ten thousand rats are coming this way—
The Lord forgive you for yesterday!"

"I'll go to my tower on the Rhine," replied he,
" 'Tis the safest place in Germany;
The walls are high, and the shores are steep,
And the stream is strong, and the water deep."

Bishop Hatto fearfully hasten'd away,
And he cross'd the Rhine without delay,
And reach'd his tower, and barr'd with care
All the windows, doors, and loopholes there.

He laid him down and closed his eyes,
But soon a scream made him arise;
He started, and saw two eyes of flame
On his pillow from whence the screaming came.

He listen'd and look'd; it was only the cat;
But the Bishop he grew more fearful for that,
For she sat screaming, mad with fear,
At the army of rats that was drawing near.

For they have swum over the river so deep,
And they have climb'd the shores so steep,
And up the tower their way is bent
To do the work for which they were sent.

They are not to be told by the dozen or score,
By thousands they come, and by myriads and more;

Such numbers had never been heard of before,
Such a judgment had never been witness'd of yore.

Down on his knees the Bishop fell,
And faster and faster his beads did he tell,
As louder and louder drawing near
The gnawing of their teeth he could hear.

And in at the windows, and in at the door,
And through the walls helter-skelter they pour,
And down from the ceiling, and up through the floor,
From the right and the left, from behind and before,

From within and without, from above and below,
And all at once to the Bishop they go.

They have whetted their teeth against the stones,
And now they pick the Bishop's bones;
They gnaw'd the flesh from every limb,
For they were sent to do judgment on him.

ROBERT SOUTHEY

How Bill Went East

A LEGEND OF THE ARGONAUTS

'Twas out in California in the days of Forty-Nine,
Two Yankee men were partners in the Dolly Varden mine;
And Jim was right as ninepence, but poor Bill began to pine.
  (This is gospel, friends, I'm telling you.)

When Bill had grown so feeble that he'd taken to his bed,
One day he called Jim to him and "Good-by, Old Pard," he said;
"You'll have to plant me far from home"—and then his spirit fled.
  (And Jim felt powerful lonely.)

Jim pondered on Bill's words, and then at last, "By Time," said he,
"Bill was the squarest partner that I ever hope to see.
I'll plant him back in Yankeeland—that's where he wants to be."
  (That showed some feeling, didn't it?)

Jim tried to send Bill homewards on a Yankee sailing ship;
With Bill aboard, the sailors said they wouldn't make the trip;
The purser wouldn't purse a bit, the skipper wouldn't skip.
  (A superstitious lot, they were.)

But Jim was nothing daunted, and a sturdy cask he found.
He put Old Bill inside it, and packed seaweed all around;
And soon Old Bill in this disguise for Yankeeland was bound.
  (This may sound fishy, but it isn't.)

That sailing ship beat round the Horn, through storms that crossed
    her way;
She made her port in Yankeeland, though after long delay;
And so Jim's cask in safety reached Bill's relatives one day.
   (Quite a journey for Bill, too.)

On that very day Aunt Hetty gained the age of eighty-three.
Her neighbors were assembled there to hold a jamboree;
They wondered what the contents of the battered cask might be.
   ("I'm so *curious*," remarked one lady.)

Dear Auntie Hetty only beamed on each inquiring guest.
"I think," she said, "it's something from my nephew in the West;
He used to tell of all his aunts he liked Aunt Het the best."
   ("Such vanity—at *her* age!" whispered another lady.)

They stood and speculated as to what the cask might hold;
It hefted rather heavy, yet it seemed too light for gold;
Then, "Open it," said Auntie, and they did as they were told.
   ("A lot of pesky seaweed," complained one man.)

And there sat Bill inside it, just as lifelike as you please,
Excepting that his whiskers hung a foot below his knees.
"I swan!" cried Auntie Hetty. "Will was always such a tease!"
   (She didn't faint, or anything.)

GEORGE S. BRYAN

There Lived a King

There lived a King, as I've been told,
In the wonder-working days of old,
When hearts were twice as good as gold,
   And twenty times as mellow.
Good temper triumphed in his face,
And in his heart he found a place

For all the erring human race
   And every wretched fellow.
When he had Rhenish wine to drink
It made him very sad to think
That some, at junket or at jink,
   Must be content with toddy.
He wished all men as rich as he
(And he was rich as rich could be),
So to the top of every tree
   Promoted everybody.

Lord Chancellors were cheap as sprats,
And Bishops in their shovel hats
Were plentiful as tabby cats—
   In point of fact, too many.
Ambassadors cropped up like hay,
Prime Ministers and such as they
Grew like asparagus in May,
   And Dukes were three a penny.
On every side Field Marshals gleamed,
Small beer were Lords Lieutenant deemed,
With Admirals the ocean teemed,
   All round his wide dominions;
And Party Leaders you might meet
In twos and threes in every street,
Maintaining, with no little heat,
   Their various opinions.

That King, although no one denies
His heart was of abnormal size,
Yet he'd have acted otherwise
   If he had been acuter.
The end is easily foretold,
When every blessed thing you hold
Is made of silver, or of gold,
   You long for simple pewter.
When you have nothing else to wear
But cloth of gold and satins rare,

For cloth of gold you cease to care—
    Up goes the price of shoddy.
In short, whoever you may be,
To this conclusion you'll agree,
When everyone is somebodee,
    Then no one's anybody!

W. S. GILBERT

But Then

John Oswald McGuffin he wanted to die
    'Nd bring his career to an end;
Of course, well—he didn't say nothin' to me—
    But that's what he told every friend.
So one afternoon he went down to the pier,
'Nd folks saw him actin' most terribly queer;
He prayed 'nd he sung, put his hand up to cough
An' everyone thought he was a-goin to jump off—
        But he didn't.
        He may jump tomorrer
        Mornin' at ten—
        Said he was goin' to
        Try it again—
        But then.

John Oswald he said he was tired of the earth—
    Of its turmoil and struggle and strife—
'Nd he made up his mind a long, long time ago
    He was just bound t' take his own life;
'Nd the very next time 'at he started to shave,
Determined to die, he wus goin' t' be brave;
So he stood up 'nd flourished the knife in despair
'Nd everyone thought 'at he 'd kill himself there—
        But he didn't.
        He says 'at tomorrer
        Mornin' at ten

He has a notion to
Try it again—
But then.

He went and bought arsenic, bought paris green,
   'Nd cobalt 'nd all kinds of stuff,
'Nd he took great delight in leaving it 'round—
   Of course that was done for a bluff—
Then he rigged up his room with a horrible thing
That would blow his head off by pullin' a string.
Folks heard the explosion—rushed up—on his bed
John Oswald was lyin'. They whispered, "He's dead."
   But he wasn't.
   He riz up 'nd said:
   Couldn't say when
   He'd fully decide to
   Try it again—
   But then.

BEN KING

Dow's Flat

Dow's Flat. That's its name;
   And I reckon that you
   Are a stranger? The same?
   Well, I thought it was true—
For thar isn't a man on the river as can't spot the place at first
   view.

It was called after Dow—
   Which the same was an ass—
   And as to the how
   Thet the thing kem to pass—
Jest tie up your hoss to that buckeye, and sit ye down here in the
   grass.

You see this 'yer Dow
         Hed the worst kind of luck;
     He slipped up somehow
         On each thing thet he struck.
Why, ef he'd a straddled thet fence rail, the derned thing 'd get up
     and buck.

     He mined on the bar
         Till he couldn't pay rates;
     He was smashed by a car
         When he tunneled with Bates;
And right on the top of his trouble kem his wife and five kids
     from the States.

     It was rough—mighty rough;
         But the boys they stood by,
     And they brought him the stuff
         For a house, on the sly;
And the old woman—well, she did washing, and took on when no
     one was nigh.

     But this 'yer luck of Dow's
         Was so powerful mean
     That the spring near his house
         Dried right up on the green;
And he sunk forty feet down for water, but nary a drop to be seen.

     Then the bar petered out,
         And the boys wouldn't stay;
     And the chills got about,
         And his wife fell away;
But Dow in his well kept a peggin' in his usual ridikilous way.

     One day—it was June—
         And a year ago, jest—
     This Dow kem at noon
         To his work like the rest,
With a shovel and pick on his shoulder, and derringer hid in his
     breast.

He goes to the well,
    And he stands on the brink,
And stops for a spell
    Jest to listen and think:
For the sun in his eyes (jest like this, sir!), you see, kinder made
    the cuss blink.

His two ragged gals
    In the gulch were at play,
And a gownd that was Sal's
    Kinder flapped on a bay:
Not much for a man to be leavin', but his all—as I've heer'd the
    folks say.

And—That's a pert hoss
    Thet you've got—ain't it now?
What might be her cost?
    Eh? Oh!—Well, then, Dow—
Let's see—well, that forty-foot grave wasn't his, sir, that day,
    anyhow.

For a blow of his pick
    Sorter caved in the side,
And he looked and turned sick,
    Then he trembled and cried.
For you see the dern cuss had struck—"Water?"—Beg your pard-
    ing, young man—there you lied!

In was *gold*—in the quartz,
    And it ran all alike;
And I reckon five oughts
    Was the worth of that strike;
And that house with the coopilow's his'n,—which the same isn't
    bad for a Pike.

Thet's why it's Dow's Flat;
    And the thing of it is
That he kinder got that
    Through sheer contrairiness:

For 'twas *water* the derned cuss was seekin', and his luck made
  him certain to miss.

            Thet's so! Thar's your way,
                To the left of yon tree;
            But—a—look h'yur, say?
                Won't you come up to tea?
No? Well, then the next time you're passin'; and ask after Dow—
  and thet's *me*.

BRET HARTE

The Fair Circassian

            Forty viziers saw I go
            Up to the Seraglio,
            Burning, each and every man,
            For the fair Circassian.

            Ere the morn had disappeared,
            Every vizier wore a beard;
            Ere the afternoon was born,
            Every vizier came back shorn.

            "Let the man that woos to win
            Woo with an unhairy chin":
            Thus she said, and as she bid
            Each devoted vizier did.

            From the beards a cord she made,
            Looped it to the balustrade,
            Glided down and went away
            To her own Circassia.

            When the Sultan heard, waxed he
            Somewhat wroth, and presently

In the noose themselves did lend
Every vizier did suspend.

Sages all, this rhyme who read,
Of your beards take prudent heed,
And beware the wily plans
Of the fair Circassians.

RICHARD GARNETT

Dorlan's Home Walk

The ninth; last half; the score was tied,
  The hour was big with fate,
For Neal had fanned and Kling had flied
  When Dorlan toed the plate.

And every rooter drew a breath
  And rose from where he sat,
For weal or woe, or life or death
  Now hung on Dorlan's bat.

The pitcher scowled; the pitcher flung
  An inshoot, swift and queer;
But Dorlan whirled his wagon-tongue
  And smote the leathern sphere.

He smote the ball with might and main,
  He drove it long and low,
And firstward like a railway train
  He sped to beat the throw.

He reached first base with time to spare
  (The throw went high and wide),

But what a tumult rent the air
   When "Safe!" the umpire cried.

"What!" shrieked the pitcher, lean and tall,
   "What!" roared the catcher stout,
"Wha-at!" yelled the basemen one and all,
   "Ye're off! the man is out!"

The shortstop swore, the catcher pled,
   They waved their arms around.
The umpire shook his bullet-head
   And sternly held his ground,

Though in the wild-eyed fielders ran
   To tear him limb from limb
Or else to tell that erring man
   Just what they thought of *him*.

The basemen left the bases clear
   And came to urge their case—
So Dorlan yawned and scratched his ear
   And strolled to second base.

"Safe? Safe?" the pitcher hissed. "Ye're blind!"
   And breathed a naughty word;
While Dorlan hitched his belt behind
   And rambled on to third.

And throats were hoarse and words ran high
   And lips were flecked with foam,
As Dorlan scanned the azure sky
   And ambled on toward home.

And still he heard in dreamy bliss,
   As down the line he came,
The umpire growl, "Enough o' this!
   He's safe. Now play the game!"

"All right. Come, boys," the pitcher bawled,
 "Two out; now make it three!"
When Dorlan touched the plate and drawled,
 "Hey! score that run fer me!"

What wrath was there, what bitter talk,
 What joy and wild acclaim!
For Dorlan's peaceful homeward walk
 Had won the doubtful game.

Aye, thus the game was lost and won;
 So, athletes, great and small,
If like mischance ye fain would shun
 Keep cool, don't kick, play ball.

ARTHUR GUITERMAN

In Church

"And now to God the Father," he ends,
And his voice thrills up to the topmost tiles:
Each listener chokes as he bows and bends,
And emotion pervades the crowded aisles.
Then the preacher glides to the vestry door,
And shuts it, and thinks he is seen no more.

The door swings softly ajar meanwhile,
And a pupil of his in the Bible class,
Who adores him as one without gloss or guile,
Sees her idol stand with a satisfied smile
And re-enact at the vestry glass
Each pulpit gesture in deft dumb show
That had moved the congregation so.

THOMAS HARDY

The Cremation of Sam McGee

There are strange things done in the midnight sun
  By the men who moil for gold;
The Arctic trails have their secret tales
  That would make your blood run cold;   Slow
The Northern Lights have seen queer sights,
  But the queerest they ever did see,
Was that night on the marge of Lake Lebarge
  I cremated Sam McGee.   Slow

Now Sam McGee was from Tennessee, where the cotton blooms
  and blows.
Why he left his home in the South to roam 'round the Pole,
  God only knows.
He was always cold, but the land of gold seemed to hold him
  like a spell;
Though he'd often say in his homely way that "he'd sooner live
  in hell."

On a Christmas day we were mushing our way over the Dawson
  trail.
Talk of your cold! through the parka's fold it stabbed like a
  driven nail.
If our eyes we'd close, then the lashes froze till sometimes we
  couldn't see;
It wasn't much fun, but the only one to whimper was Sam
  McGee.

And that very night, as we lay packed tight in our robes beneath
  the snow,
And the dogs were fed, and the stars o'erhead were dancing
  heel and toe,
He turned to me, and "Cap," says he, "I'll cash in this trip, I
  guess;
And if I do, I'm asking that you won't refuse my last request."

[93]

Well, he seemed so low that I couldn't say no; then he says with
    a sort of moan:
"It's the cursèd cold, and it's got right hold till I'm chilled clean
    through to the bone.
Yet 'tain't being dead—it's my awful dread of the icy grave that
    pains;
So I want you to swear that, foul or fair, you'll cremate my last
    remains."

A pal's last need is a thing to heed, so I swore I would not fail;
And we started on at the streak of dawn; but God! he looked
    ghastly pale.
He crouched on the sleigh, and he raved all day of his home in
    Tennessee;
And before nightfall a corpse was all that was left of Sam
    McGee.

Slow

There wasn't a breath in that land of death, and I hurried, horror-
    driven,
With a corpse half hid that I couldn't get rid, because of a
    promise given;
It was lashed to the sleigh, and it seemed to say: "You may tax
    your brawn and brains,
But you promised true, and it's up to you to cremate these last
    remains."

Now a promise made is a debt unpaid, and the trail has its own
    stern code.
In the days to come, though my lips were dumb, in my heart how
    I cursed that load.
In the long, long night, by the lone firelight, while the huskies,
    round in a ring,
Howled out their woes to the homeless snows—O God! how I
    loathed the thing.

And every day that quiet clay seemed to heavy and heavier grow;
And on I went, though the dogs were spent and the grub was
    getting low;

The trail was bad, and I felt half mad, but I swore I would not
  give in;
And I'd often sing to the hateful thing, and it hearkened with a
  grin.

Till I came to the marge of Lake Lebarge, and a derelict there
  lay;
It was jammed in the ice, but I saw in a trice it was called the
  Alice May.
And I looked at it, and I thought a bit, and I looked at my frozen
  chum;
Then "Here," said I, with a sudden cry, "is my cre-ma-tor-eum."

Some planks I tore from the cabin floor, and I lit the boiler fire;
Some coal I found that was lying around, and I heaped the
  fuel higher;
The flames just soared, and the furnace roared—such a blaze
  you seldom see;
And I burrowed a hole in the glowing coal, and I stuffed in Sam
  McGee.

Then I made a hike, for I didn't like to hear him sizzle so;
And the heavens scowled, and the huskies howled, and the wind
  began to blow.
It was icy cold, but the hot sweat rolled down my cheeks, and I
  don't know why;
And the greasy smoke in an inky cloak went streaking down the
  sky.

I do not know how long in the snow I wrestled with grisly fear;
But the stars came out and they danced about ere again I
  ventured near;
I was sick with dread, but I bravely said: "I'll just take a peep
  inside.
I guess he's cooked, and it's time I looked"; . . . then the door I
  opened wide.

And there sat Sam, looking cool and calm, in the heart of the
  furnace roar;

And he wore a smile you could see a mile, and he said: "Please
    close that door.
It's fine in here, but I greatly fear you'll let in the cold and
    storm—
Since I left Plumtree down in Tennessee, it's the first time I've
    been warm."

There are strange things done in the midnight sun
  By the men who moil for gold;
The Arctic trails have their secret tales
  That would make your blood run cold;
The Northern Lights have seen queer sights,
  But the queerest they ever did see
Was that night on the marge of Lake Lebarge
  I cremated Sam McGee.

ROBERT W. SERVICE

The Microscope

Anton Leeuwenhoek was Dutch.
He sold pincushions, cloth, and such.
The waiting townsfolk fumed and fussed
As Anton's dry goods gathered dust.

He worked, instead of tending store,
At grinding special lenses for
A microscope. Some of the things
He looked at were:
                mosquitoes' wings,
the hairs of sheep, the legs of lice,
the skin of people, dogs, and mice;
ox eyes, spiders' spinning gear,
fishes' scales, a little smear
of his own blood,
          and best of all,

the unknown, busy, very small
bugs that swim and bump and hop
inside a simple water drop.

Impossible! most Dutchmen said.
This Anton's crazy in the head.
We ought to ship him off to Spain.
He says he's seen a housefly's brain.
He says the water that we drink
Is full of bugs. He's mad, we think!

They called him *dummkopf,* which means dope.
That's how we got the microscope.

MAXINE KUMIN

Henry VIII

Bluff King Hal was full of beans;
He married half a dozen queens;
For three called Kate they cried the banns,
And one called Jane, and a couple of Annes.

The first he asked to share his reign
Was Kate of Aragon, straight from Spain—
But when his love for her was spent,
He got a divorce, and out she went.

Anne Boleyn was his second wife;
He swore to cherish her all his life—
But seeing a third he wished instead,
He chopped off poor Anne Boleyn's head.

He married the next afternoon
Jane Seymour, which was rather soon—

But after one year as his bride
She crept into her bed and died.

Anne of Cleves was Number Four;
Her portrait thrilled him to the core—
But when he met her face to face
Another royal divorce took place.

Catherine Howard, Number Five,
Billed and cooed to keep alive—
But one day Henry felt depressed;
The executioner did the rest.

Sixth and last came Catherine Parr,
Sixth and last and luckiest far—
For this time it was Henry who
Hopped the twig, and a good job too.

ELEANOR and HERBERT FARJEON

In Hardin County, 1809

With flintlocked guns and polished stocks,
Knee breeches and long homespun socks,
On morning of St. Valentine
Two hunters met in 1809
Across the line from Illinois;
They stopped their mules and voiced their joy.

"Why, Ben, it's been quite a spell
Since I've seen you. The folks all well?
Bring any news from up near town?"
"Why, yes. D'you know John Ezry Brown?
They say that he's a-goin down
To Washington in all the din
To see Jim Madison sworn in.

"And this young feller Bonaparte
That's fightin' cross the sea,
Is slicin' Europe all to bits.
Least that's what they're a tellin' me."
"Wal, wal, nice day, kinda breezy,
This mule's gettin' quite uneasy.

"Now come and see us some time, do,
And bring the gals and Hepsy, too."
"Yes, some fine day we'll be along,
Got any news to send along?"
"No, nothin' worth a tinker's song.
There's nothin' happens here near me,
Doggondest place you ever see.

"Tom Lincoln lives right over there,
In that log cabin, bleak and bare,
They say they have a little babe,
I understand they've named him 'Abe.'
Yes, Sally said just 'tother day,
That nothin' happens down this way."

                              LULU E. THOMPSON

The Blacksmith's Serenade

John Littlehouse the redhead was a large ruddy man
Quite proud to be a blacksmith, and he loved Polly Ann, Polly
    Ann.
Straightway to her window with his iron guitar he came
Breathing like a blacksmith—his wonderful heart's flame.
Though not very bashful and not very bold
He had reached the plain conclusion his passion must be told.
And so he sang: "Awake, awake,"—this hip-hoo-ray-ious man.
"Do you like me, do you love me, Polly Ann, Polly Ann?
The rooster on my coal shed crows at break of day.

It makes a person happy to hear his roundelay.
The fido in my woodshed barks at fall of night.
He makes one feel so safe and snug. He barks exactly right.
I swear to do my stylish best and purchase all I can
Of the flummeries, flunkeries, and mummeries of man.
And I will carry in the coal and the water from the spring
And I will sweep the porches if you will cook and sing.
No doubt your Pa sleeps like a rock. Of course Ma is awake
But dares not say she hears me, for gentle custom's sake.
Your sleeping father knows I am a decent honest man.
Will you wake him, Polly Ann,
And if he dares deny it I will thrash him, lash bash mash
Hash him, Polly Ann.
Hum hum hum, fee fie fo fum—
And my brawn should wed your beauty.
Do you hear me, Polly Ann, Polly Ann?"

Polly had not heard of him before, but heard him now.
She blushed behind the shutters like a pippin on the bough.
She was not overfluttered, she was not overbold.
She was glad a lad was living with a passion to be told.
But she spoke up to her mother: "Oh, what an awful man:—"
This merry merry quite contrary tricky trixy, Polly Ann, Polly
    Ann.
The neighbors put their heads out of the windows. They said:—
"What sort of turtle dove is this that seems to wake the dead?"
Yes, in their nighties whispered this question to the night.
They did not dare to shout it. It wouldn't be right.
And so, I say, they whispered:—"Does she hear this awful man,
Polly Ann, Polly Ann?"

John Littlehouse the redhead sang on of his desires:
"Steel makes the wires of lyres, makes the frames of terrible
    towers
And circus chariots' tires.
Believe me, dear, a blacksmith man can feel.
I will bind you, if I can, to my ribs with hoops of steel.
Do you hear me, Polly Ann, Polly Ann?"

And then his tune was silence, for he was not a fool.
He let his voice rest, his iron guitar cool.
And thus he let the wind sing, the stars sing and the grass sing,
The prankishness of love sing, the girl's tingling feet sing,
Her trembling sweet hands sing, her mirror in the dark sing,
Her grace in the dark sing, her pillow in the dark sing,
The savage in her blood sing, her starved little heart sing,
Silently sing.

"Yes, I hear you, Mister Man,"
To herself said Polly Ann, Polly Ann.

He shouted one great loud *"Good night,"* and laughed,
And skipped home.
And every star was winking in the wide wicked dome.

And early in the morning, sweet Polly stole away.
And though the town went crazy, she is his wife today.

VACHEL LINDSAY

Off the Ground

Three jolly farmers
Once bet a pound
Each dance the others would
Off the ground.

Out of their coats
They slipped right soon,
And neat and nicesome,
Put each his shoon.

One—two—three!—
And away they go,
Not too fast,

And not too slow:
Out from the elm tree's
Noonday shadow,
Into the sun
And across the meadow.
Past the schoolroom,
With knees well bent,
Fingers a-flicking,
They dancing went.
Up sides and over,
And round and round,
They crossed click-clacking
The parish bound.
By Tupman's meadow
They did their mile,
Tee-to-tum
On a three-barred stile.
Then straight through Whipham,
Downhill to Week,
Footing it lightsome,
But not too quick,
Up fields to Watchet,
And on through Wye,
Till seven fine churches
They'd seen skip by—
Seven fine churches,
And five old mills,
Farms in the valley,
And sheep on the hills;
Old Man's Acre
And Dead Man's Pool
All left behind,
As they danced through Wool.

And Wool gone by,
Like tops that seem
To spin in sleep
They danced in dream:

Withy—Wellover—
Wassop—Wo—
Like an old clock
Their heels did go.
A league and a league
And a league they went.
And not one weary,
And not one spent.
And lo! and behold!
Past Willow-cum-Leigh
Stretched with its waters
The great green sea.

Says Farmer Bates,
"I puffs and I blows,
What's under the water,
Why, no man knows!"
Says Farmer Giles,
"My wind comes weak,
And a good man drownded
Is far to seek."
But Farmer Turvey,
On twirling toes
Ups with his gaiters,
And in he goes:
Down where the mermaids
Pluck and play
On their twangling harps
In a sea-green day;
Down where the mermaids,
Finned and fair,
Sleek with their combs
Their yellow hair. . . .
Bates and Giles—
On the shingle sat,
Gazing at Turvey's
Floating hat.
But never a ripple

Nor bubble told
Where he was supping
Off plates of gold.
Never an echo
Rilled through the sea
Of the feasting and dancing
And minstrelsy.
They called—called—called:
Came no reply:
Nought but the ripples'
Sandy sigh.
Then glum and silent
They sat instead,
Vacantly brooding
On home and bed,
Till both together
Stood up and said:—
"Us knows not, dreams not,
Where you be,
Turvey, unless
In the deep blue sea;
But axcusing silver—
And it comes most willing—
Here's us two paying
Our forty shilling;
For it's sartin sure, Turvey,
Safe and sound,
You danced us square, Turvey,
Off the ground!"

WALTER DE LA MARE

Grandfather Watts's Private Fourth

Grandfather Watts used to tell us boys
That a Fourth wa'n't a Fourth without any noise.
He would say, with a thump of his hickory stick,

That it made an American right down *sick*
To see his sons on the Nation's Day
Sit round, in a sort of a listless way,
With no oration and no train band,
No firework show and no root-beer stand;
While his grandsons, before they were out of bibs,
Were ashamed—Great Scott!—to fire off squibs.

And so, each Independence morn,
Grandfather Watts took his powder horn,
And the flintlock shotgun *his* father had
When he fought under Schuyler, a country lad;
And Grandfather Watts would start and tramp
Ten miles to the woods at Beaver Camp;
For Grandfather Watts used to say—and scowl—
That a decent chipmunk, or woodchuck, or owl
Was better company, friendly or shy,
Than folks who didn't keep Fourth of July.
And so he would pull his hat down on his brow,
And march for the woods, sou'-east by sou'.

But once—ah, long, long years ago,
For Grandfather's gone where good men go—
One hot, hot Fourth, by ways of our own
(Such shortcuts as boys have always known),
We hurried, and followed the dear old man
Beyond where the wilderness began—
To the deep black woods at the foot of the Hump;
And there was a clearing—and a stump.

A stump in the heart of a great wide wood,
And there on that stump our Grandfather stood,
Talking and shouting out there in the sun,
And firing that funny old flintlock gun
Once in a minute—his head all bare—
Having his Fourth of July out there:
The Fourth of July that he used to know,
Back in eighteen-and-twenty or so!

First, with his face to the heavens blue,
He read the "Declaration" through;
And then, with gestures to left and right,
He made an oration erudite,
Full of words six syllables long—
And then our Grandfather burst into song!
And, scaring the squirrels in the trees,
Gave "Hail, Columbia!" to the breeze.

And I tell you the old man never heard
When we joined in the chorus word for word!
But he sang out strong to the bright blue sky;
And if voices joined in his Fourth of July,
He heard them as echoes from days gone by.

And when he had done, we all slipped back,
As still as we came, on our twisting track,
While words more clear than the flintlock shots
Rang in our ears.
        And Grandfather Watts?

He shouldered the gun his father bore,
And marched off home, nor'-west by nor'.

H. C. BUNNER

Richard Cory

Whenever Richard Cory went downtown,
We people on the pavement looked at him:
He was a gentleman from sole to crown,
Clean favored, and imperially slim.

And he was always quietly arrayed,
And he was always human when he talked;
But still he fluttered pulses when he said,
"Good morning," and he glittered when he walked.

And he was rich—yes, richer than a king—
And admirably schooled in every grace:
In fine, we thought that he was everything
To make us wish that we were in his place.

So on we worked, and waited for the light,
And went without the meat, and cursed the bread;
And Richard Cory, one calm summer night,
Went home and put a bullet through his head.

EDWIN ARLINGTON ROBINSON

Moloney Remembers the Resurrection of Kate Finucane

"O she was the handsome corpse," he said,
"Divil a difference between livin' and dead
You'd see in her; a fine red face
On a starchy pillow edged with lace,
Her cold hands clasped, her mousy hair
As 'neatly tied as a girl's at a fair.
Touchin' forty she was when she passed away,
But twenty she looked as she lay
In bed on the broad of her back.
Kate Finucane of Asdee West
Was stretched in death, but she looked her best!

          Her cousins had come
From all parts of the Kingdom
For the wake; Coffeys and Lanes from Dingle,
McCarthys and Ryans, married and single,
Honest and otherwise. For a day and a night
As she lay in her bed, a sight
For sore eyes, they drank and they prayed
And they sang her to heaven—as fine
A wake as ever I went to in all my time!

Well, there was nothin' to do, after prayin' and drinkin',
But lift herself into the coffin.
'Twas at that moment, glory to God,
As I stood with my glass at the head
Of her bed, that she stretched like a cat and opened her eyes
And lifted her head in great surprise;
And motherogod will I ever forget
The cut an' the go, the sight an' the set˙
Of her when, calm as you like, with a toss of her head,
Kate Finucane sat up in the bed!

                    No need to tell
Of all the confusion that fell
On the cousins, neighbors, myself, and the house.
Dead she'd been, and now this disastrous
Return to life, upsettin' the whole
Place, and I thinkin' her body was lackin' a soul.
But after a while, things quietened down
And Kate made tea for the cousins. She found
She'd not seen them for ages. What's more,
She clapped her eye on a Lenamore
Man called Harty, and three months later,
Paraded him in rare style up to the altar!
On top o' that, she showed the world she could
Make a dandy wife, for she's still to the good,
And without doubt or favor, fright or fear,
Kate Finucane has a child a year!

"Gay woman, Kate," Moloney said,
"Divil a difference between livin' and dead!"

BRENDAN KENNELLY

The Mountain Whippoorwill

OR, HOW HILLBILLY JIM
WON THE GREAT FIDDLERS' PRIZE
(A GEORGIA ROMANCE)

Up in the mountains, it's lonesome all the time,
(Sof' win' slewin' thu' the sweet-potato vine).

Up in the mountains, it's lonesome for a child,
(Whippoorwills a-callin' when the sap runs wild).

Up in the mountains, mountains in the fog,
Everythin's as lazy as an old houn' dog.

Born in the mountains, never raised a pet,
Don't want nuthin' an' never got it yet.

Born in the mountains, lonesome-born,
Raised runnin' ragged thu' the cockleburrs and corn.

Never knew my pappy, mebbe never should.
Think he was a fiddle made of mountain laurel wood.

Never had a mammy to teach me pretty-please.
Think she was a whippoorwill, a-skitin' thu' the trees.

Never had a brother ner a whole pair of pants,
But when I start to fiddle, why, yuh got to start to dance!

Listen to my fiddle—Kingdom Come—Kingdom Come!
Hear the frogs a-chunkin' "Jug o' rum, Jug o' rum!"
Hear that mountain-whippoorwill be lonesome in the air,
An' I'll tell yuh how I traveled to the Essex County Fair.

Essex County has a mighty pretty fair,
All the smarty fiddlers from the South come there.

Elbows flyin' as they rosin up the bow
For the first Prize Contest in the Georgia Fiddlers' Show.

Old Dan Wheeling, with his whiskers in his ears,
Kingpin fiddler for nearly twenty years.

Big Tom Sargent, with his blue walleye,
An' Little Jimmy Weezer that can make a fiddle cry.

All sittin' roun', spittin' high an' struttin' proud,
(Listen, little whippoorwill, yuh better bug yore eyes!)
Tun-a-tun-tunin' while the jedges told the crowd
Them that got the mostest claps 'd win the bestest prize.

Everybody waitin' for the first tweedle-dee,
When in comes a-stumblin'—hillbilly me!

Bowed right pretty to the jedges an' the rest,
Took a silver dollar from a hole inside my vest,

Plunked it on the table an' said, "There's my callin' card!
An' anyone that licks me—well, he's got to fiddle hard!"

Old Dan Wheeling, he was laughin' fit to holler,
Little Jimmy Weezer said, "There's one dead dollar!"

Big Tom Sargent had a yaller-toothy grin,
But I tucked my little whippoorwill spang underneath my chin,
An' petted it an' tuned it till the jedges said, "Begin!"

Big Tom Sargent was the first in line;
He could fiddle all the bugs off a sweet-potato vine.

He could fiddle down a possum from a mile-high tree.
He could fiddle up a whale from the bottom of the sea.

Yuh could hear hands spankin' till they spanked each other raw,
When he finished variations on "Turkey in the Straw."

Little Jimmy Weezer was the next to play;
He could fiddle all night, he could fiddle all day.

He could fiddle chills, he could fiddle fever,
He could make a fiddle rustle like a lowland river.

He could make a fiddle croon like a lovin' woman.
An' they clapped like thunder when he'd finished strummin'.

Then came the ruck of the bobtailed fiddlers,
The let's-go-easies, the fair-to-middlers.

They got their claps an' they lost their bicker,
An' settled back for some more corn licker.

An' the crowd was tired of their no-count squealing,
When out in the center steps Old Dan Wheeling.

He fiddled high and he fiddled low,
(Listen, little whippoorwill; yuh got to spread yore wings!)
He fiddled with a cherrywood bow.
(Old Dan Wheeling's got bee honey in his strings.)

He fiddled the wind by the lonesome moon,
He fiddled a most almighty tune.

He started fiddling like a ghost,
He ended fiddling like a host.

He fiddled north an' he fiddled south,
He fiddled the heart right out of yore mouth.

He fiddled here an' he fiddled there.
He fiddled salvation everywhere.

When he was finished, the crowd cut loose,
(Whippoorwill, they's rain on yore breast.)
An' I sat there wonderin', "What's the use?"
(Whippoorwill, fly home to yore nest.)

But I stood up pert an' I took my bow,
An' my fiddle went to my shoulder, so.

An'—they wasn't no crowd to get me fazed—
But I was alone where I was raised.

Up in the mountains, so still it makes yuh skeered,
Where God lies sleepin' in his big white beard.

An' I heard the sound of the squirrel in the pine,
An' I heard the earth a-breathin' thu' the long nighttime.

They've fiddled the rose an' they've fiddled the thorn,
But they haven't fiddled the mountain corn.

They've fiddled sinful an' fiddled moral,
But they haven't fiddled the breshwood laurel.

They've fiddled loud, an' they've fiddled still,
But they haven't fiddled the whippoorwill.

I started off with a *dump-diddle-dump*,
(*Oh, Hell's broke loose in Georgia!*)
Skunk cabbage growin' by the bee-gum stump,
(*Whippoorwill, yo're singin' now!*)

Oh, Georgia booze is mighty fine booze,
The best yuh ever poured yuh,
But it eats the soles right offen yore shoes,
For Hell's broke loose in Georgia.

My mother was a whippoorwill pert,
My father, he was lazy,
But I'm Hell broke loose in a new store shirt
To fiddle all Georgia crazy.

Swing yore partners—up an' down the middle!
Sashay now—oh, listen to that fiddle!
Flapjacks flippin' on a red-hot griddle,
An' Hell broke loose,
Hell broke loose,
Fire on the mountains—snakes in the grass.
Satan's here a-bilin'—oh, Lordy, let him pass!
Go down Moses, set my people free,
Pop goes the weasel thu' the old Red Sea!
Jonah sittin' on a hickory bough,

Up jumps a whale—an' where's yore prophet now?
Rabbit in the pea patch, possum in the pot,
Try an' stop my fiddle, now my fiddle's gettin' hot!
Whippoorwill, singin' thu' the mountain hush,
Whippoorwill, shoutin' from the burnin' bush,
Whippoorwill, cryin' in the stable door,
Sing tonight as yuh never sang before!
Hell's broke loose like a stompin' mountain shoat,
Sing till yuh bust the gold in yore throat!
Hell's broke loose for forty miles aroun'
Bound to stop yore music if yuh don't sing it down.
Sing on the mountains, little whippoorwill,
Sing to the valleys, an' slap 'em with a hill,
For I'm struttin' high as an eagle's quill,
An' Hell's broke loose,
Hell's broke loose,
Hell's broke loose in Georgia!

They wasn't a sound when I stopped bowin',
(*Whippoorwill, yuh can sing no more.*)
But, somewhere or other, the dawn was growin',
(*Oh, mountain whippoorwill!*)

An' I thought, "I've fiddled all night an' lost.
Yo're a good hillbilly, but yuh've been bossed."

So I went to congratulate old man Dan,
—But he put his fiddle into my han'—
An' then the noise of the crowd began.

STEPHEN VINCENT BENÉT

When I Brought the News

I thought I was going to be a millionaire. With moroccan bound
books for looks everywhere. And even a drive that went for a

mile through the trees and little lakes and lilies. So in my best serious face I stood in line for the job and told the nervous man I'd work very hard.

Every afternoon loaded down I set off on the outskirts of town folding papers with a sleight of hand and flicking them across the gray porches. And even in an open window for a laugh which I thought I needed. And as I proceeded along this frontier road picking berries grapes and peaches I said hi to the rival newspaper boy and told him he was underpaid and you'll never make the money I've made. But it was a lie.

Because Friday I collected and most said come back tomorrow and I objected but turned my sad face away and mumbled it was only a dime. And you'd think it was a crime every time I rang a doorbell and even those with chimes and added up the weeks they owed. In there they sit warm and reading, with smells of steak and pizza pie. Out here lips chapped with frost I might die, dancing on my cold toes. There's only so much I can stand, you savage hearts.

But I was glad at times along here in sun on these quiet roads where some buildings were built in the sky out of trees and near the river. The green the grass the cliffs and hills and bridges bent over the trains. Cool summer halls to click heels and spin down the stairs on my educated wrist. Noisy with the news. And deep in my own unsavage heart I loved nothing better than delivery.

And Saturdays in autumn afternoon kicking through the leaves I came to ring the bell and knock on the door and say I beg you pay me please. And the heads with after-lunch eyes came out too beaten to refuse. In my little book I marked them paid and with some quiet charm of mine I tried to make them feel it was not the end of the world. And maybe there would be a new woman's page soon. Or a competition for a prize.

But some heartless called me liar and lingerer. Napping under trees, banging on doors and a whistler in halls. I whispered something about freedom and they shouted don't come back no more and slammed the door. I walked away with young tears melting with despair. They'd all be sorry when they found me Christmas Eve shoeless and starved, dead in the snow.

And weeks went by till one Sunday dawn in black winter I brought my pencil. I wrote across the front page HOW DOES IT FEEL TO CHEAT A CHILD. And tucked the paper carefully in the door. Monday creeping through the streets I saw the raging faces watching from windows everywhere and a man on a porch shaking a fist which he said would break my head. And fearful but forceful I told him drop dead. And ran.

I prayed for spring when I could sing once more and steal the cooling cooky from a windowsill. With the sun such a fat red thing up in the sky. And count my blessings instead of money. But things were sad instead of sunny when Mr. Brown screeched up in his sporty car. I wore my slack jaw. He wagged a finger, confound you D, the News is deluged with complaints, your public relations are a scandal, the customers claim you're a nuisance and a vandal and did you write how does it feel to cheat a child? I did. Confound you D, don't you know the customer is always right? Come along with me and apologize. I said no. He said so, you're fired.

Never to bring the news again. Or trap a customer on the street or write my editorial across the front page. A failed millionaire with no moroccan bound books for looks anywhere.

J. P. DONLEAVY

Heather Ale

A GALLOWAY LEGEND

From the bonny bells of heather
    They brewed a drink long-syne,
Was sweeter far than honey,
    Was stronger far than wine.
They brewed it and they drank it,
    And lay in a blessed swound
For days and days together
    In their dwellings underground.

There rose a king in Scotland,
    A fell man to his foes,
He smote the Picts in battle,
    He hunted them like roes.
Over miles of the red mountain
    He hunted as they fled,
And strewed the dwarfish bodies
    Of the dying and the dead.

Summer came in the country,
    Red was the heather bell;
But the manner of the brewing
    Was none alive to tell.
In graves that were like children's
    On many a mountain head,
The Brewsters of the Heather
    Lay numbered with the dead.

The king in the red moorland
    Rode on a summer's day;
And the bees hummed, and the curlews
    Cried beside the way.
The king rode, and was angry,
    Black was his brow and pale,
To rule in a land of heather
    And lack the Heather Ale.

It fortuned that his vassals,
    Riding free on the heath,
Came on a stone that was fallen
    And vermin hid beneath.
Rudely plucked from their hiding,
    Never a word they spoke:
A son and his aged father—
    Last of the dwarfish folk.

The king sat high on his charger,
    He looked on the little men;

And the dwarfish and swarthy couple
   Looked at the king again.
Down by the shore he had them;
   And there on the giddy brink—
"I will give you life, ye vermin,
   For the secret of the drink."

There stood the son and father
   And they looked high and low;
The heather was red around them,
   The sea rumbled below.
And up and spoke the father,
   Shrill was his voice to hear:
"I have a word in private,
   A word for the royal ear.

"Life is dear to the aged,
   And honor a little thing;
I would gladly sell the secret,"
   Quoth the Pict to the King.
His voice was small as a sparrow's,
   And shrill and wonderful clear:
"I would gladly sell my secret,
   Only my son I fear.

"For life is a little matter,
   And death is nought to the young;
And I dare not sell my honor
   Under the eye of my son.
Take *him*, O king, and bind him,
   And cast him far in the deep;
And it's I will tell the secret
   That I have sworn to keep."

They took the son and bound him,
   Neck and heels in a thong,
And a lad took him and swung him,
   And flung him far and strong,

And the sea swallowed his body,
  Like that of a child of ten;—
And there on the cliff stood the father,
  Last of the dwarfish men.

"True was the word I told you:
  Only my son I feared;
For I doubt the sapling courage
  That goes without the beard.
But now in vain is the torture,
  Fire shall never avail:
Here dies in my bosom
  The secret of Heather Ale."

ROBERT LOUIS STEVENSON

Simon Soggs' Thanksgiving

"Let Earth give thanks," the deacon said,
And then the proclamation read.

"Give thanks fer what an' what about?"
Asked Simon Soggs when church was out.
"Give thanks fer what? I don't see why;
The rust got in an' spiled my rye,
And hay wan't half a crop, and corn
All wilted down and looked forlorn.
The bugs jest gobbled my petaters,
The what-you-call-em lineaters,
And gracious! when you come to wheat,
There's more than all the world can eat;
Onless a war should interfere,
Crops won't bring half a price this year;
I'll hev to give 'em away, I reckon!"
"Good for the poor!" exclaimed the deacon.

"Give thanks fer what?" asked Simon Soggs.
"Fer th' freshet carryin' off my logs?
Fer Dobbin goin' blind? Fer five
Uv my best cows, that was alive
Afore the smashin' railroad come
And made it awful troublesome?
Fer that haystack the lightnin' struck
And burnt to ashes?—thund'rin luck!
For ten dead sheep?" sighed Simon Soggs.
The Deacon said, "You've got yer hogs!"

"Give thanks? and Jane and baby sick?
I e'enmost wonder if ole Nick
Ain't runnin' things!"

                  The deacon said,
"Simon! yer people might be dead!"
"Give thanks!" said Simon Soggs again.
"Jest look at what a fix we're in!
The country's rushin' to the dogs
At racehorse speed!" said Simon Soggs.

"Rotten all through—in every state—
Why, ef we don't repudiate,
We'll hev to build, fer big and small,
A poorhouse that'll hold us all.
All round the crooked whisky still
Is runnin' like the Devil's mill;
Give thanks? How mad it makes me feel,
To think how office-holders steal!
The taxes paid by you and me
Is four times bigger'n they should be;
The Fed'ral Gov'ment's all askew,
The ballot's sech a mockery, too!
Some votes too little, some too much,
Some not at all—it beats the Dutch!
And now no man knows what to do,

Or how is how, or who is who.
Deacon! corruption's sure to kill!
This 'glorious Union' never will,
I'll bet a continental cent,
Elect another President!
Give thanks fer what, I'd like to know?"

The deacon answered, sad and low,
"Simon! It fills me with surprise,
Ye don't see where yer duty lies;
Kneel right straight down, in all the muss,
And thank God that it ain't no wuss!"

W. A. CROFFUT

Birds,
Beasts,
and Bugs

Sheep

When I was once in Baltimore,
   A man came up to me and cried,
"Come, I have eighteen hundred sheep,
   And we will sail on Tuesday's tide.

"If you will sail with me, young man,
   I'll pay you fifty shillings down;
These eighteen hundred sheep I take
   From Baltimore to Glasgow town."

He paid me fifty shillings down,
   I sailed with eighteen hundred sheep;
We soon had cleared the harbor's mouth,
   We soon were in the salt sea deep.

The first night we were out at sea
   Those sheep were quiet in their mind;
The second night they cried with fear—
   They smelt no pastures in the wind.

They sniffed, poor things, for their green fields,
   They cried so loud I could not sleep:
For fifty thousand shillings down
   I would not sail again with sheep.

W. H. DAVIES

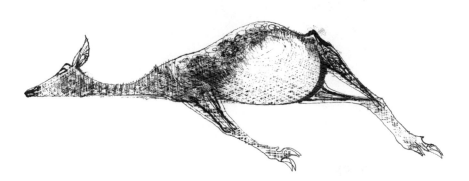

Traveling Through the Dark

Traveling through the dark I found a deer
dead on the edge of the Wilson River road.
It is usually best to roll them into the canyon:
that road is narrow; to swerve might make more dead.

By glow of the taillight I stumbled back of the car
and stood by the heap, a doe, a recent killing;
she had stiffened already, almost cold.
I dragged her off; she was large in the belly.

My fingers touching her side brought me the reason—
her side was warm; her fawn lay there waiting,
alive, still, never to be born.
Beside that mountain road I hesitated.

The car aimed ahead its lowered parking lights;
under the hood purred the steady engine.
I stood in the glare of the warm exhaust turning red;
around our group I could hear the wilderness listen.

I thought hard for us all—my only swerving—
then pushed her over the edge into the river.

WILLIAM STAFFORD

The Twa Corbies

As I was walking all alane
I heard twa corbies* making a mane;
The tane unto the t'other say,
"Where sall we gang and dine today?

"—In behint yon auld fail* dyke
I wot there lies a new-slain knight;
And naebody kens that he lies there,
But his hawk, and hound, and lady fair.

"His hound is to the hunting gane,
His hawk to fetch the wildfowl hame,
His lady's ta'en another mate,
So we may mak our dinner sweet.

"Ye'll sit on his white hause-bane,*
And I'll pick out his bonnie blue een:
Wi' ae lock o' his gowden hair
We'll theek our nest when it grows bare.

"Mony a one for him makes mane,
But nane sall ken where he is gane;
O'er his white banes, when they are bare,
The wind sall blaw for evermair."

OLD SCOTTISH BALLAD

* corbies: ravens
* fail: turf
* hause-bane: neck bone

The Trap

"That red fox,
Back in the furthest field,

Caught in my hidden trap,
Was half mad with fear.
During the night
He must have ripped his foot
From the cold steel.
I saw him early this morning,
Dragging his hurt leg,
Bleeding a path across the gold wheat,
Whining with the pain,
His eyes like cracked marbles.
I followed as he moved,
His thin body pulled to one side
In a weird helplessness.
He hit the wire fence,
Pushing through it
Into the deep, morning corn,
And was gone."
The old man looked around the kitchen
To see if anyone was listening.
"Crazy red fox,
Will kill my chickens no longer.
Will die somewhere in hiding."
He lit the brown tobacco carefully,
Watching the blue smoke rise and disappear
In the movement of the air.
Scratching his red nose slowly,
Thinking something grave for a long moment,
He stared out of the bright window.
"He won't last long with that leg," he said.
The old man turned his head
To see if his wife was listening.
But she was deep in thought,
Her stained fingers
Pressing red berries in a pie.
He turned his white head
Toward the open window again.
"Guess I'll ride into the back field, first thing.

Some mighty big corn back there this year.
Mighty big corn."
His wife looked up from her work,
Smiled almost secretly to herself,
And finished packing the ripe berries
Into the pale crust.

WILLIAM BEYER

The Glory Trail

'Way high up the Mogollons,
   Among the mountaintops,
A lion cleaned a yearlin's bones
   And licked his thankful chops,
When on the picture who should ride,
   A-trippin' down a slope,
But High-Chin Bob, with sinful pride
   And mav'rick-hungry rope.

   "Oh, glory be to me," says he,
     "And fame's unfadin' flowers!
   All meddlin' hands are far away;
   I ride my good top-hawse today
   And I'm top-rope of the Lazy J—
     Hi! kitty cut, you're ours!"

That lion licked his paw so brown
   And dreamed soft dreams of veal—
And then the circlin' loop sung down
   And roped him 'round his meal.
He yowled quick fury to the world
   Till all the hills yelled back;
The top-hawse gave a snort and whirled
   And Bob caught up the slack.

"Oh, glory be to me," laughs he.
  "We've hit the glory trail.
No human man as I have read
Darst loop a ragin' lion's head,
Nor ever hawse could drag one dead
  Until we told the tale."

'Way high up the Mogollons
  That top-hawse done his best,
Through whippin' brush and rattlin' stones,
  From canyon-floor to crest.
But ever when Bob turned and hoped
  A limp remains to find,
A red-eyed lion, belly roped
  But healthy, loped behind.

"Oh, glory be to me," grunts he.
  "This glory trail is rough,
Yet even till the Judgment Morn
I'll keep this dally 'round the horn,
For never any hero born
  Could stoop to holler: 'Nuff!' "

Three suns had rode their circle home
  Beyond the desert's rim,
And turned their star-herds loose to roam
  The ranges high and dim;
Yet up and down and 'round and 'cross
  Bob pounded, weak and wan,
For pride still glued him to his hawse
  And glory drove him on.

"Oh, glory be to me," sighs he.
  "He kaint be drug to death,
But now I know beyond a doubt
Them heroes I have read about
Was only fools that stuck it out
  To end of mortal breath."

'Way high up the Mogollons
  A prospect man did swear
That moon dreams melted down his bones
  And hoisted up his hair:
A ribby cow-hawse thundered by,
  A lion trailed along,
A rider, ga'nt but chin on high,
  Yelled out a crazy song.

  "Oh, glory be to me!" cries he,
    "And to my noble noose!
  Oh, stranger, tell my pards below
  I took a rampin' dream in tow,
  And if I never lay him low,
    I'll never turn him loose!"

BADGER CLARK

The Rescue

The boy climbed up into the tree.
The tree rocked. So did he.
He was trying to rescue a cat.
A cushion of a cat, from where it sat
In a high crutch of branches, mewing
As though to say to him, "Nothing doing,"
Whenever he shouted, "Come on, come down."
So up he climbed, and the whole town
Lay at his feet, round him the leaves
Fluttered like a lady's sleeves,
And the cat sat, and the wind blew so
That he would have flown had he let go.
At last he was high enough to scoop
That fat white cushion or nincompoop
And tuck her under his arm and turn
        To go down—
                But oh! he began to learn

How high he was, how hard it would be.
Having come up with four limbs, to go down with three.
His heartbeats knocked as he tried to think:
He would put the cat in a lower chink—
She appealed to him with a cry of alarm
And put her eighteen claws in his arm.
So he stayed looking down for a minute or so,
To the good ground so far below.
When the minute began he saw it was hard;
When it ended he couldn't move a yard.
So there he was stuck, in the failing light
And the wind rising with the coming of the night.

His father! He shouted for all he was worth.
His father came nearer: "What on earth—?"
"I've got the cat up here but I'm stuck."
"Hold on . . . ladder . . ." he heard. O luck!
How lovely behind the branches tossing
The globes at the pedestrian crossing
And the big fluorescent lamps glowed
Mauve-green on the main road.
But his father didn't come back, didn't come;
His little fingers were going numb.
The cat licked them as though to say,
"Are you feeling cold? I'm O.K."
He wanted to cry, he would count ten first,
But just as he was ready to burst
A torch came and his father and mother
And a ladder and the dog and his younger brother.
Up on a big branch stood his father,
His mother came to the top of the ladder,
His brother stood on a lower rung,
The dog sat still and put out its tongue.
From one to the other the cat was handed
And afterwards she was reprimanded.
After that it was easy, though the wind blew:
The parents came down, the boy come too

From the ladder, the lower branch, and the upper,
And all of them went indoors to supper,
And the tree rocked, and the moon sat
In the high branches like a white cat.

HAL SUMMERS

Kentucky Belle

Summer of 'sixty-three, sir, and Conrad was gone away—
Gone to the country town, sir, to sell our first load of hay.
We lived in the log house yonder, poor as ever you've seen;
Roschen there was a baby, and I was only nineteen.

Conrad, he took the oxen, but he left Kentucky Belle;
How much we thought of Kentuck, I couldn't begin to tell—
Came from the Bluegrass country; my father gave her to me
When I rode north with Conrad, away from the Tennessee.

Conrad lived in Ohio—a German he is, you know—
The house stood in broad cornfields, stretching on, row after row;
The old folks made me welcome; they were kind as kind could be;
But I kept longing, longing, for the hills of the Tennessee.

O, for a sight of water, the shadowed slope of a hill!
Clouds that hang on the summit, a wind that never is still!
But the level land went stretching away to meet the sky—
Never a rise from north to south, to rest the weary eye!

From east to west, no river to shine out under the moon,
Nothing to make a shadow in the yellow afternoon;
Only the breathless sunshine, as I looked out, all forlorn,
Only the "rustle, rustle," as I walked among the corn.

When I fell sick with pining we didn't wait any more,

But moved away from the cornlands out to this river shore—
The Tuscarawas it's called, sir—off there's a hill, you see—
And now I've grown to like it next best to the Tennessee.

I was at work that morning. Someone came riding like mad
Over the bridge and up the road—Farmer Rouf's little lad.
Bareback he rode; he had no hat; he hardly stopped to say,
"Morgan's men are coming, Frau, they're galloping on this way.

"I'm sent to warn the neighbors. He isn't a mile behind;
He sweeps up all the horses—every horse that he can find;
Morgan, Morgan the raider, and Morgan's terrible men,
With bowie knives and pistols, are galloping up the glen."

The lad rode down the valley, and I stood still at the door—
The baby laughed and prattled, playing with spools on the floor;
Kentuck was out in the pasture; Conrad, my man, was gone;
Near, near Morgan's men were galloping, galloping on!

Sudden I picked up baby and ran to the pasture bar:
"Kentuck!" I called; "Kentucky!" She knew me ever so far!
I led her down the gully that turns off there to the right,
And tied her to the bushes; her head was just out of sight.

As I ran back to the log house at once there came a sound—
The ring of hoofs, galloping hoofs, trembling over the ground,
Coming into the turnpike out from the White-Woman Glen—
Morgan, Morgan the raider, and Morgan's terrible men.

As near they drew and nearer my heart beat fast in alarm;
But still I stood in the doorway, with baby on my arm.
They came; they passed; with spur and whip in haste they sped
    along;
Morgan, Morgan the raider, and his band six hundred strong.

Weary they looked and jaded, riding through night and through
    day;

Pushing on east to the river, many long miles away,
To the border strip where Virginia runs up into the west,
And for the Upper Ohio before they could stop to rest.

On like the wind they hurried, and Morgan rode in advance;
Bright were his eyes like live coals, as he gave me a sideways
      glance;
And I was just breathing freely, after my choking pain,
When the last one of the troopers suddenly drew his rein.

Frightened I was to death, sir; I scarce dared look in his face,
As he asked for a drink of water and glanced around the place;
I gave him a cup, and he smiled—'twas only a boy, you see,
Faint and worn, with dim blue eyes; and he'd sailed on the Ten-
    nessee.

Only sixteen he was, sir—a fond mother's only son—
Off and away with Morgan before his life had begun!
The damp drops stood on his temples; drawn was the boyish
      mouth;
And I thought me of the mother waiting down in the South!

O, plucky was he to the backbone and clear grit through and
      through;
Boasted and bragged like a trooper; but the big words wouldn't do;
The boy was dying, sir, dying, as plain as plain could be,
Worn out by his ride with Morgan up from the Tennessee.

But, when I told the laddie that I too was from the South,
Water came in his dim eyes and quivers around his mouth.
"Do you know the Bluegrass country?" he wistful began to say,
Then swayed like a willow sapling and fainted dead away.

I had him into the log house, and worked and brought him to;
I fed him and coaxed him, as I thought his mother'd do;
And, when the lad got better, and the noise in his head was gone,
Morgan's men were miles away, galloping, galloping on.

"O, I must go," he muttered; " I must be up and away!
Morgan, Morgan is waiting for me! O, what will Morgan say?"
But I heard a sound of tramping and kept him back from the
    door—
The ringing sound of horses' hoofs that I had heard before.

And on, on came the soldiers—the Michigan cavalry—
And fast they rode, and black they looked galloping rapidly;
They had followed hard on Morgan's track; they had followed day
    and night;
But of Morgan and Morgan's raiders they had never caught a
    sight.

And rich Ohio sat startled through all those summer days,
For strange, wild men were galloping over her broad highways;
Now here, now there, now seen, now gone, now north, now east,
    now west,
Through river valleys and cornland farms, sweeping away her best.

A bold ride and a long ride! But they were taken at last.
They almost reached the river by galloping hard and fast;
But the boys in blue were upon them ere ever they gained the
    ford,
And Morgan, Morgan the raider, laid down his terrible sword.

Well, I kept the boy till evening—kept him against his will—
But he was too weak to follow, and sat there pale and still;
When it was cool and dusky—you'll wonder to hear me tell—
But I stole down to that gully and brought up Kentucky Belle.

I kissed the star on her forehead—my pretty, gentle lass—
But I knew that she'd be happy back in the old Bluegrass;
A suit of clothes of Conrad's, with all the money I had,
And Kentuck, pretty Kentuck, I gave to the worn-out lad.

I guided him to the southward as well as I knew how;
The boy rode off with many thanks, and many a backward bow;

And then the glow it faded, and my heart began to swell,
As down the glen away she went, my lost Kentucky Belle!

When Conrad came in the evening the moon was shining high;
Baby and I were both crying—I couldn't tell him why—
But a battered suit of rebel gray was hanging on the wall,
And a thin old horse with drooping head stood in Kentucky's stall.

Well, he was kind, and never once said a hard word to me;
He knew I couldn't help it—'twas all for the Tennessee;
But, after the war was over, just think what came to pass—
A letter, sir; and the two were safe back in the old Bluegrass.

The lad had got across the border, riding Kentucky Belle;
And Kentuck she was thriving, and fat, and hearty, and well;
He cared for her, and kept her, nor touched her with whip or
    spur:
Ah! we've had many horses, but never a horse like her!

CONSTANCE FENIMORE WOOLSON

The Fox

The fox went out on a chilly night,
Prayed to the moon for to give him light,
For he'd many a mile to go that night
    Afore he reached the town-o.

He ran till he came to a great big bin;
The ducks and the geese were put therein.
"A couple of you will grease my chin,
    Afore I leave this town-o."

He grabbed the gray goose by the neck,
Throwed a duck across his back;

He didn't mind the "quack, quack, quack"
    And the legs a-dangling down-o.

Then old mother Flipper-Flopper jumped out of bed,
Out of the window she stuck her head,
Crying, "John! John! The gray goose is gone
    And the fox is on the town-o!"

Then John, he went to the top of the hill,
Blowed his horn both loud and shrill;
The fox, he said, "I better flee with my kill
    Or they'll soon be on my trail-o."

He ran till he came to his cozy den,
There were the little ones eight, nine, ten.
They said, "Daddy, better go back again,
    'Cause it must be a mighty fine town-o."

Then the fox and his wife without any strife,
Cut up the goose with a fork and knife;
They never had such a supper in their life
    And the little ones chewed on the bones-o.

OLD BALLAD

small talk

i went into the flea circus
on broadway the other day
and heard a lot of fleas
talking and bragging to each other
one flea had been over to the swell dog show
and was boasting that he had bit
a high priced thoroughbred dog
yeah says another flea

that is nothing to get so proud of
a thoroughbred dog tastes just like a mongrel
i should think you would be more democratic
than to brag about that
go and get a reputation
said a third flea
i went into a circus last spring and bit a lion
i completely conquered him
i made him whine and cringe
he did not bite me back
get out of my way
i am the flea that licked a lion
i said to myself probably
that lion didnt even know he had been bitten
some insects are just like human beings
small talk i said to myself
and went away from there

archy the cockroach

DON MARQUIS

Robbing the Tree Hive

They leaned a good stout rail against the tree
And then the Old Man said: "It's up you go,
Sonny, and you blokes hold the dogs and see
That all is out of harm's way here below.

"It's that big limb you're after—have a look—
The hive is halfway out there on the right.
Cut near the trunk, and if the bees go crook,
Hang on for life and let the beggars bite."

"They sting, not bite," said Fred. The Old Man frowned:
"And what's the difference? Ready, lad? Take hold!"

One spurt of climbing took me from the ground
Up to the great smooth trunk whose bark felt cold

Under my fingers after the dry wood.
And when I reached the fork the whole tree stirred
Against my flesh as though it understood
Who touched it now was neither bee nor bird.

That made me half afraid; but I looked down
And saw the Old Man watching there below,
And felt the spur-prick of his warning frown,
And braced and swung my ax for the first blow.

That set all right, and soon my thought was running
Only upon my task, and I was proud
To feel in wrist and hand the axman's cunning
That sent the chips down in a whirring crowd.

I knew the bees were pouring from their spout,
But kept on with my chopping, left and right,
And left again, until I heard the shout:
"She's coming! Drop your ax and hang on tight!"

The trunk seemed going over with the weight
Of the sprung limb, but stopped and twisted free,
And shuddered like a man, and jerked back straight
The broken half of what had been a tree.

Below, the men were running in to smoke
The bees with burning rags. I laughed aloud
To hear their voices stutter to a choke,
And see them come out gasping from their cloud.

But overhead the sky was very still—
The sky I'd made then when my ax went home—
And I but sat and stared at that until
The Old Man called me down to taste the comb.

ERNEST G. MOLL

A Story

After they passed I climbed
out of my hole and sat
in the sun again. Loose rocks
all around make it safe—I can
hear anyone moving. It often
troubles me to think how others
dare live where stealth is possible,
and how they can feel safe, considering
all the narrow places,
without whiskers.

Anyway, those climbers were a puzzle—
above where I live nothing lives.
And they never came down. There is no
other way. The way it is,
they crawl far before they die.
I make my hole the deepest one
this high on the mountainside.

WILLIAM STAFFORD

The Dog's Cold Nose

When Noah, perceiving 'twas time to embark,
Persuaded the creatures to enter the Ark,
The dog, with a friendliness truly sublime,
Assisted in herding them. Two at a time
He drove in the elephants, zebras and gnus
Until they were packed like a boxful of screws,
The cat in the cupboard, the mouse on the shelf,
The bug in the crack; then he backed in himself.
But such was the lack of available space

He couldn't tuck all of him into the place;
So after the waters had flooded the plain
And down from the heavens fell blankets of rain
He stood with his muzzle thrust out through the door
The whole forty days of that terrible pour!
Because of which drenching, zoologists hold,
The nose of a healthy dog always is cold!

ARTHUR GUITERMAN

Twin Lakes Hunter

Last night a freezing cottontail
Slept just outside our outside door
And drew upon the heat that leaked
Through threshold from the floor.

Rex, the hunter told me so.
"Cold out," he said. "Some storm!"
He hoped the little fellow
Slept snug enough and warm.

He backed up to the Monarch range,
A-shiver in his mackinaw.
"I been outside an hour," he said.
"Take me a week to thaw."

"Snug, so you can shoot him later?"
He answered, "Please don't scold.
It's just I can't abide the thought
Of dying from the cold."

A. B. GUTHRIE, JR.

The Zebra Dun

We were camped on the plains at the head of the Cimarron
When along came a stranger and stopped to arger some,
He seemed so very foolish that we began to look around,
We thought he was a greenhorn that had just 'scaped from town.

We asked if he'd been to breakfast; he hadn't had a smear,
So we opened up the chuck-box and bade him have his share.
He took a cup of coffee and some biscuits and some beans,
And then began to talk and tell about foreign kings and queens—

About the Spanish war and the fighting on the seas
With guns as big as steers and ramrods big as trees—
And about Old Paul Jones, a mean, fighting son of a gun,
Who was the grittiest cuss that ever pulled a gun.

Such an educated feller, his thoughts just came in herds,
He astonished all them cowboys with them jaw-breaking words.
He just kept on talking till he made the boys all sick,
And they began to look around just how to play a trick.

He said that he had lost his job upon the Santa Fé
And was going across the plains to strike the 7-D.
He didn't say how come it, some trouble with the boss,
But said he'd like to borrow a nice fat saddle hoss.

This tickled all the boys to death, they laughed down in their
    sleeves—
"We'll lend you a horse just as fresh and fat as you please."
Shorty grabbed a lariat and roped the Zebra Dun,
Turned him over to the stranger and waited for the fun.

Old Dunny was a rocky outlaw that had grown so awful wild
That he could paw the white out of the moon every jump for a
    mile.

Old Dunny stood right still—as if he didn't know—
Until he was saddled and ready for to go.

When the stranger hit the saddle, old Dunny quit the earth
And traveled right straight up for all that he was worth.
A-pitching and a-squealing, a-having walleyed fits,
His hind feet perpendicular, his front ones in the bits.

We could see the tops of the mountains under Dunny every jump,
But the stranger he was growed there just like the camel's hump;
The stranger sat upon him and curled his black mustache
Just like a summer boarder waiting for his hash.

[145]

He thumped him in the shoulders and spurred him when he
    whirled,
To show them flunky punchers that he was the wolf of the
    world.
When the stranger had dismounted once more upon the ground,
We knew he was a thoroughbred and not a gent from town.

The boss who was standing round, a-watching of the show,
Walked right up to the stranger and told him he needn't go—
"If you can use the lasso like you rode old Zebra Dun,
You're the man I've been looking for ever since the year of one."

Oh, he could twirl the lariat and he didn't do it slow,
He could catch them forefeet nine out of ten for any kind of
    dough.
And when the herd stampeded he was always on the spot
And set them to nothing, like the boiling of a pot.

There's one thing and a shore thing I've learned since I've been
    born,
That every educated feller ain't a plumb greenhorn.

AMERICAN COWBOY BALLAD

Caprice

It wasn't intended that the cow should find the poppies.
    (There are many, many places where red poppies grow
In the maize, in the wheat, in the green hay meadows;
    If you look in under, you can see them—so.)

The white cow went in there because the hedge was broken.
    (She was a milk-colored cow with huge brown eyes,
And she smelled sweet as milk, as she walked with heavy udders.)
    She sniffed the hay meadow with pleased surprise.

She ate the green hay and she ate the red poppies;
  She lay down to rest and to chew her cud,
And to eat them again with reminiscent rapture—
  The poppy and the pod and the sheathed round bud.

Of course she dreamed—having eaten poppies!
  She walked the silver thoroughfare that is the Milky Way.
She had never seen cypresses, but certainly cypresses
  Hemmed the road in, slender and gray.

And the sky was lavender, and dusty with mystery.
  She dreamed that she was Io, walking there
In a shift of silk and a damask tunic
  With scarlet flowers in her long gold hair.

She knew that she was Io! Dearie, dearie,
  She was so lovely and slim and white,
That the god who looked on her loved her straightway,
  And leaned to caress her. Her heart was light

On her lips as she kissed him; but it seemed very quiet,
  And she wondered if his house had straw on the floor—
It is wise for cows to avoid red poppies.
  She can never be happy any more.

DOROTHY STOTT SHAW

the flattered lightning bug

a lightning bug got
in here the other night a
regular hick from
the real country he was
awful proud of himself you
city insects may think
you are some punkins

but i don t see any
of you flashing in the dark
like we do in
the country all right go
to it says i mehitabel the
cat and that green
spider who lives in your locker
and two or three cockroach
friends of mine and a
friendly rat all gathered
around him and urged him on
and he lightened and
lightened and lightened you
don t see anything like this
in town often he says go to it
we told him it s a
real treat to us and
we nicknamed him broadway
which pleased him
this is the life
he said all i
need is a harbor
under me to be a
statue of liberty and
he got so vain of
himself i had to take
him down a peg you ve
made lightning for two hours
little bug i told him
but i don t hear
any claps of thunder
yet there are some men
like that when he wore
himself out mehitabel
the cat ate him

                archy

DON MARQUIS

Adventures
and Disasters

The Luck of Edenhall

Of Edenhall, the youthful Lord
Bids sound the festal trumpet's call.
He rises at the banquet board,
And cries, 'mid the drunken revelers all,
"Now bring me the Luck of Edenhall!"

The butler hears the words with pain,
The house's oldest seneschal,
Takes slow from its silken cloth again
The drinking glass of crystal tall;
They call it the Luck of Edenhall.

Then said the Lord, "This glass to praise,
Fill with red wine from Portugal!"
The graybeard with trembling hand obeys;
A purple light shines over all,
It beams from the Luck of Edenhall.

Then speaks the Lord, and waves it light,
"This glass of flashing crystal tall
Gave to my sires the Fountain Sprite;
She wrote in it, *If this glass doth fall,*
Farewell then, O Luck of Edenhall!

" 'Twas right a goblet the Fate should be
Of the joyous race of Edenhall!
Deep draughts drink we right willingly;
And willingly ring, with merry call,
Kling! klang! to the Luck of Edenhall!"

First rings it deep, and full, and mild,
Like to the song of a nightingale;
Then like the roar of a torrent wild;
Then mutters at last like the thunder's fall,
The glorious Luck of Edenhall.

"For its keeper takes a race of might,
The fragile goblet of crystal tall;
It has lasted longer than is right;
Kling! klang!—with a harder blow than all
Will I try the Luck of Edenhall!"

As the goblet ringing flies apart,
Suddenly cracks the vaulted hall;
And through the rift, the wild flames start;
The guests in dust are scattered all,
With the breaking Luck of Edenhall!

In storms the foe, with fire and sword;
He in the night had scaled the wall,
Slain by the sword lies the youthful Lord,
But holds in his hand the crystal tall,
The shattered Luck of Edenhall.

On the morrow the butler gropes alone,
The graybeard in the desert hall,
He seeks his Lord's burnt skeleton,
He seeks in the dismal ruin's fall
The shards of the Luck of Edenhall.

"The stone wall," saith he, "doth fall aside,
Down must the stately columns fall;

Glass is this earth's Luck and Pride;
In atoms shall fall this earthy ball
One day like the Luck of Edenhall!"

HENRY WADSWORTH LONGFELLOW

A Longford Legend

Oh! 'tis of a bold major a tale I'll relate,
Who possessed a fine house and a charming estate,
Who, when possible, always his pleasure would take
From morning till night in a boat on his lake.
So a steam launch he bought from a neighboring peer,
And learnt how to start her, to stoke, and to steer;
But part of the craft he omitted to learn—
How to ease her, and to stop her, and back her astern.

Well, one lovely spring morn from the moorings they cast,
The furnace alight and the steam in full blast.
As they cruised through the lake, oh! what pleasure was theirs!
What congratulations! what swagger! what airs!
"Evening's come," says the major: "let's home for the night.
I'll pick up the mooring and make her all right;
Whilst you, my gay stoker, your wages to earn,
Just ease her, and stop her, and back her astern."

"Do what?" asked the stoker. "Why, stop her, of course!"
"Faith! it's aisier stopping a runaway horse!
Just try it yourself!" the field officer swore.
But that was no use—they were nearly on shore!
He swore at himself, at the boat, and the crew;
He cursed at the funnel, the boiler, the screw—
But in vain! He was forced from his mooring to turn,
Shouting, "Ease her, and stop her, and back her astern!"

It was clear that on shore they that night would not dine,
So they drank up the brandy, the whisky and wine;
They finished the stew and demolished the cake
As they steamed at full speed all the night round the lake.
Weeks passed; and with terror and famine oppressed,
One by one of that ill-fated crew sank to rest;
And grim death seized the major before he could learn
How to ease her, and stop her, and back her astern.

And still round the lake their wild course they pursue,
While the ghost of the major still swears at the crew,
And the ghosts of the crew still reply in this mode,
"Just ease her, and stop her yourself—and be blowed!"
Here's the moral: Imprimis, whene'er you're afloat,
Don't use haughty words to your crew on your boat;
And ere starting, oh! make this your deepest concern—
Learn to ease her, and stop her, and back her astern.

IRISH BALLAD

Flannan Isle

"Though three men dwell on Flannan Isle
To keep the lamp alight,
As we steered under the lee, we caught
No glimmer through the night."

A passing ship at dawn had brought
The news; and quickly we set sail,
To find out what strange thing might ail
The keepers of the deep-sea light.

The winter day broke blue and bright,
With glancing sun and glancing spray,
While o'er the swell our boat made way,
As gallant as a gull in flight.

But as we neared the lonely Isle,
And looked up at the naked height,
And saw the lighthouse towering white,
With blinded lantern, that all night
Had never shot a spark
Of comfort through the dark,
So ghostly in the cold sunlight
It seemed, that we were struck the while
With wonder all too dread for words.

And as into the tiny creek
We stole beneath the hanging crag,
We saw three queer, black, ugly birds—
Too big, by far, in my belief,
For cormorant or shag—
Like seamen sitting bolt upright
Upon a half-tide reef:
But, as we neared, they plunged from sight,
Without a sound, or spurt of white.

And still too mazed to speak,
We landed; and made fast the boat;
And climbed the track in single file,
Each wishing he were safe afloat,
On any sea, however far,
So it be far from Flannan Isle:
And still we seemed to climb, and climb,
As though we'd lost all count of time,
And so must climb for evermore.
Yet, all too soon, we reached the door—
The black, sun-blistered lighthouse door,
That gaped for us ajar.

As, on the threshold, for a spell,
We paused, we seemed to breathe the smell
Of limewash and of tar,
Familiar as our daily breath,
As though 'twere some strange scent of death:
And so, yet wondering, side by side,
We stood a moment, still tongue-tied:
And each with black foreboding eyed
The door, ere we should fling it wide,
To leave the sunlight for the gloom:
Till, plucking courage up, at last,
Hard on each other's heels we passed,
Into the living room.

Yet, as we crowded through the door,
We only saw a table, spread
For dinner, meat and cheese and bread;
But, all untouched; and no one there:
As though, when they sat down to eat,
Ere they could even taste,
Alarm had come; and they in haste
Had risen and left the bread and meat:
For at the table-head a chair
Lay tumbled on the floor.

We listened; but we only heard
The feeble cheeping of a bird
That starved upon its perch:
And, listening still, without a word,
We set about our hopeless search.

We hunted high, we hunted low;
And soon ransacked the empty house;
Then o'er the Island, to and fro,
We ranged, to listen and to look
In every cranny, cleft, or nook
That might have hid a bird or mouse:
But, though we searched from shore to shore,
We found no sign in any place:
And soon again stood face to face
Before the gaping door:
And stole into the room once more
As frightened children steal.

Ay: though we hunted high and low,
And hunted everywhere,
Of the three men's fate we found no trace
Of any kind in any place,
But a door ajar, and an untouched meal,
And an overtoppled chair.

And as we listened in the gloom
Of that forsaken living room—
A chill clutch on our breath—
We thought how ill-chance came to all
Who kept the Flannan Light:
And how the rock had been the death
Of many a likely lad:
How six had come to a sudden end,
And three had gone stark mad:
And one whom we'd all known as friend
Had leapt from the lantern one still night,

And fallen dead by the lighthouse wall:
And long we thought
On the three we sought,
And of what might yet befall.

Like curs a glance has brought to heel,
We listened, flinching there:
And looked, and looked, on the untouched meal,
And the overtoppled chair.

We seemed to stand for an endless while,
Though still no word was said,
Three men alive on Flannan Isle,
Who thought on three men dead.

W. W. GIBSON

Street Scene

A helicopter in the sky
   Observed the traffic down below,
Establishing the where and why
   Of anything that stopped the flow.

A motorist in a crawling queue,
   Distracted by the whirring rotor,
Looked up to get a better view
   And rammed (of course) another motor.

Policemen worked for half the day
   To clear things, and at last succeeded.
The helicopter whirled away
   To see where else it might be needed.

PETER SUFFOLK

The Forsaken

I

Once in the winter
Out on a lake
In the heart of the northland,
Far from the Fort
And far from the hunters,
A Chippewa woman
With her sick baby
Crouched in the last hours
Of a great storm.
Frozen and hungry,
She fished through the ice
With a line of the twisted
Bark of the cedar,
And a rabbit-bone hook
Polished and barbed;
Fished with the bare hook
All through the wild day,
Fished and caught nothing;
While the young chieftain
Tugged at her breasts,
Or slept in the lacings
Of the warm *tikanagan*.
All the lake surface
Streamed with the hissing
Of millions of iceflakes
Hurled by the wind;
Behind her the round
Of a lonely island
Roared like a fire
With the voice of the storm
In the deeps of the cedars.
Valiant, unshaken,
She took of her own flesh,

[159]

Baited the fishhook,
Drew in a gray trout,
Drew in his fellows,
Heaped them beside her,
Dead in the snow.
Valiant, unshaken,
She faced the long distance,
Wolf-haunted and lonely,
Sure of her goal
And the life of her dear one:
Tramped for two days,
On the third in the morning,
Saw the strong bulk
Of the Fort by the river,
Saw the woodsmoke
Hang soft in the spruces,
Heard the keen yelp
Of the ravenous huskies
Fighting for whitefish:
Then she had rest.

II

Years and years after,
When she was old and withered,
When her son was an old man
And his children filled with vigor,
They came in their northern tour on the verge of winter,
To an island in a lonely lake.
There one night they camped, and on the morrow
Gathered their kettles and birch bark
Their rabbit-skin robes and their mink traps,
Launched their canoes and slunk away through the islands,
Left her alone forever,
Without a word of farewell,
Because she was old and useless,
Like a paddle broken and warped,
Or a pole that was splintered.

Then, without a sigh,
Valiant, unshaken,
She smoothed her dark locks under her kerchief,
Composed her shawl in state,
Then folded her hands ridged with sinews and corded with veins,
Folded them across her breasts spent with the nourishing of children,
Gazed at the sky past the tops of the cedars,
Saw two spangled nights arise out of the twilight,
Saw two days go by filled with the tranquil sunshine,
Saw, without pain, or dread, or even a moment of longing:
Then on the third great night there came thronging and thronging
Millions of snowflakes out of a windless cloud;
They covered her close with a beautiful crystal shroud,
Covered her deep and silent.
But in the frost of the dawn,
Up from the life below,
Rose a column of breath
Through a tiny cleft in the snow,
Fragile, delicately drawn,
Wavering with its own weakness,
In the wilderness a sign of the spirit,
Persisting still in the sight of the sun
Till day was done.
Then all light was gathered up by the hand of God and hid in His breast,
Then there was born a silence deeper than silence,
Then she had rest.

DUNCAN CAMPBELL SCOTT

The Erl-King's Daughter

Sir Olf rode fast toward Thurlston's walls
To meet his bride in his father's halls.

He saw blue lights flit over the graves;
The elves came forth from their forest caves.

They dance anear on the glossy strand,
And the erl-king's daughter held out her hand.

"Oh, welcome, Sir Olf, to our jubilee!
Step into the circle, and dance with me."

"I dare not dance, I dare not stay:
Tomorrow will be my nuptial day!"

"Two golden spurs will I give to thee;
And I pray thee, Sir Olf, to tarry with me."

"I dare not tarry, I dare not delay:
Tomorrow is fixed for my nuptial day!"

"Will give thee a shirt so white and fine
Was bleached yestreen in the new moonshine."

"I dare not hearken to elf nor fay!
Tomorrow is fixed for my nuptial day."

"A measure of gold I will give unto thee;
And I pray thee, Sir Olf, to dance with me."

"The measure of gold will I carry away,
But I dare not dance, and I dare not stay."

"Then, since thou wilt go, even go with a blight!
A true-lover's token I leave thee, sir knight."

She lightly struck with her wand on his heart,
And he swooned and swooned from the deadly smart;

She lifted him up on his coal-black steed:
"Now hie thee away with a fatal speed!"

Then shone the moon, and howled the wolf,
And the sheen and the howl awoke Sir Olf.

He rode over mead, he rode over moor;
He rode till he rode to his own house door.

Within sat, white as the marble, his bride;
But his gray-haired mother stood watching outside.

"My son, my son, thou art haggard and wan!
Thy brow is the brow of a dying man."

"And haggard and wan I well may be,
For the erl-king's daughter hath wounded me."

"I pray thee, my son, dismount, and bide.
There is mist on the eyes of thy pining bride."

"O Mother! I should but drop dead from my steed.
I will wander abroad for the strength I need."

"And what shall I tell thy bride, my son,
When the morning dawns, and the tiring is done?"

"Oh, tell my bride that I rode to the wood
With my hounds in leash, and my hawk in hood."

When morning dawned with crimson and gray,
The bride came forth in her wedding array.

They poured out mead, they poured out wine:
"Now, where is thy son, O gold-mother mine?"

"My son, gold-daughter, rode into the wood,
With his hounds in leash, and his hawk in hood."

Then the bride grew sick with an ominous dread:
"Ah, woe is me! for Sir Olf is dead."

She drooped like a lily that feels the blast;
She drooped, and drooped, till she died; at last

They rest in the charnel side by side,
The stricken Sir Olf and his faithful bride.

But the erl-king's daughter dances still
Where the moonlight sleeps on the frosted hill.

JOHANN GOTTFRIED HERDER
(translated from the German by JAMES CLARENCE MANGAN)

The Dam

This was our valley, yes,
Our valley till they came
And chose to build the dam.
All the village worked on it
And we were lucky of course
All through the slump we had
Good jobs; they were too well paid
For the water rose ninety feet,

And covered our houses; yes—
In a midsummer drought
The old church spire pokes out
And the weathercock treads the wind
But we were lucky of course
We were—most of us—laid on
Like the water, to the town.
Somehow, I stayed behind.

I work on the dam, yes—
Do you think the drowned ash trees
Still have faint impulses
When Spring's up here I wonder?

I was lucky of course
But oh there's a lot of me
Feels like a stifled tree
That went on living, under.

They turn on their taps, yes,
In the dusty city and drink:
Now is it that we sink
Or that the waters rise?
They are lucky of course
But as they go to work
There's an underwater look
In their street-shuttered eyes.

This was our valley, yes,
And I live on the dam
And in my sight the dream
Still drowns the dreamer's home
But I am lucky of course
For in a time of drought
Within me and without
I see where I came from.

PATRIC DICKINSON

The Youth and the Northwind

A TALE OF NORWAY

Once on a time—'twas long ago—
  There lived a worthy dame
Who sent her son to fetch some flour,
  For she was old and lame.

But while he loitered on the road,
  The Northwind chanced to stray

Across the careless younker's path,
　　And stole the flour away.

"Alas! what shall we do for bread?"
　　Exclaimed the weeping lad;
"The flour is gone!—the flour is gone!—
　　And it was all we had!"

And so he sought the Northwind's cave,
　　Beside the distant main;
"Good Mister Boreas," said the lad,
　　"I want my flour again.

" 'Twas all we had to live upon—
　　My mother old and I;
Oh give us back the flour again,
　　Or we shall surely die!"

"I have it not," the Northwind growled;
　　"But, for your lack of bread,
I give to you this tablecloth;
　　'Twill serve you well instead;

"For you have but to spread it out,
　　And every costly dish
Will straight appear at your command,
　　Whatever you may wish."

The lad received the magic cloth
　　With wonder and delight,
And thanked the donor heartily,
　　As well, indeed, he might.

Returning homeward, at an inn
　　Just half his journey through,
He fain must show his tablecloth,
　　And what the cloth could do.

So while he slept the knavish host
    Went slyly to his bed,
And stole the cloth—but shrewdly placed
    Another in its stead.

Unknowing what the rogue had done,
    The lad went on his way,
And came unto his journey's end
    Just at the close of day.

He showed the dame his tablecloth,
    And told her of its power;
"Good sooth!" he cried, " 'twas well for us
    The Northwind stole the flour."

"Perhaps," exclaimed the cautious crone,
    "The story may be true;
'Tis mighty little good, I ween,
    Your tablecloth can do!"

And now the younker spread it forth,
    And tried the spell. Alas!
'Twas but a common tablecloth,
    And nothing came to pass.

Then to the Northwind, far away,
    He sped with might and main;
"Your tablecloth is good for naught;
    I want my flour again!"

"I have it not," the Northwind growled,
    "But, for your lack of bread,
I give to you this little goat,
    'Twill serve you well instead;

"For you have but to tell him this:
    'Make money, Master Bill!'

And he will give you golden coins,
  As many as you will."

The lad received the magic goat
  With wonder and delight,
And thanked the donor heartily,
  As well, indeed, he might.

Returning homeward, at the inn
  Just half his journey through,
He fain must show his little goat,
  And what the goat could do.

So while he slept the knavish host
  Went slyly to the shed,
And stole the goat—but shrewdly placed
  Another in his stead.

Unknowing what the rogue had done,
  The youth went on his way,
And reached his weary journey's end
  Just at the close of day.

He showed the dame his magic goat,
  And told her of his power;
"Good sooth!" he cried, " 'twas well for us
  The Northwind stole the flour."

"I much misdoubt," the dame replied,
  "Your wondrous tale is true;
'Tis little good, for hungry folk,
  Your silly goat can do!"

"Good Master Bill," the lad exclaimed,
  "Make money!" but, alas!
'Twas nothing but a common goat,
  And nothing came to pass.

Then to the Northwind, angrily,
  He sped with might and main;
"Your foolish goat is good for naught;
  I want my flour again!"

"I have it not," the Northwind growled,
  "Nor can I give you aught,
Except this cudgel—which, indeed,
  A magic charm has got;

"For you have but to tell it this:
  'My cudgel, hit away!'
And, till you bid it stop again,
  The cudgel will obey."

Returning home, he stopt at night
  Where he had lodged before;
And feigning to be fast asleep,
  He soon began to snore.

And when the host would steal the staff,
  The sleeper muttered, "Stay,
I see what you would fain be at;
  Good cudgel, hit away!"

The cudgel thumped about his ears,
  Till he began to cry,
"O stop the staff, for mercy's sake!
  Or I shall surely die!"

But still the cudgel thumped away
  Until the rascal said,
"I'll give you back the cloth and goat,
  O spare my broken head!"

And so it was the lad reclaimed
  His tablecloth and goat;

And, growing rich, at length became
   A man of famous note;

He kept his mother tenderly,
   And cheered her waning life;
And married—as you may suppose—
   A princess for a wife;

And while he lived, had ever near,
   To favor worthy ends,
A cudgel for his enemies,
   And money for his friends.

JOHN GODFREY SAXE

The Castaways

I. ISLAND NIGHTS

A Beetle, a Bat, and a Bee
Were wrecked on the Isle of Boree,
      With a barrel of gum
      And a tom-tom drum
And a hammock for each of the three.

In that lonely lugubrious place
Their life was an utter disgrace.
      The things that were done
      When the night had begun!
Shall I tell you? I haven't the face.

I would like to, but feel that I can't
When I think of your elderly aunt—
      How surprised she would be!
      How disgusted with me!
That settles the matter: I shan't.

From the desolate Isle of Boree
The Beetle, the Bat, and the Bee
    Were removed in a yacht
    That was passing the spot
As they sang, "We are castaways three!"

And her crew, with a scandalized frown,
Gave 'em all a wash-up and brush-down,
    And replacing each hat
    On Bee, Beetle, and Bat,
Delivered them safely in town.

They were given an elegant flat,
With "Welcome" inscribed on the mat,
    And a clarionet
    And a wireless set
And a knocker that said rat-a-tat.

And when people with serious looks
Brought them earnest and excellent books,
    They would speak of the Isle,
    With no sign of a smile,
As the most unattractive of nooks.

But alone, with their feet on the fender,
Their thoughts of the Island grew tender:
    "What hopes," sighed the Bat,
    "Of a wreck such as that?"
Said the Beetle: "Decidedly slender!"

"Yet gum is a wonderful drink!"
And the Bee gave the Beetle a wink;
    "So utterly lush;
    So delightfully—" "Hush!
There's a man in the passage, I think."

Time passed; and their yearning for gum
(Though the stuff is displeasing to some)
    Grew so terribly fast
    That the Beetle at last
Cried out in his agony: "Come!

Our life is a bane and a blight:
Let us sail for the Isle of Delight!
    Are you willing, my brothers?"
    "We are," said the others.
"Why not," cried the Beetle, "tonight?"

So they slipped on their Wellington boots
And their oldest and ugliest suits,
    And they opened the door,
    Threw the key on the floor,
And were off with a couple of hoots.

The sailed through the green and the blue
To the land of voluptuous glue;
    And there they remain,
    In torrents of rain.
What on earth do you think that they do?

E. V. RIEU

The Green Fiddler

As I came over the humpbacked hill
    Where the trees crowd thick and black,
I met a little old man in green
    With fiddle strapped on back.

His cap rose tall as an elfin steeple,
    His eyes shone water clear,
He bowed him low to see me go
    And he said to me, "My dear,

"It's not for silver I'm asking you,
    For shelter or meat or bread,
But pluck me four of your golden hairs,
    Four bright golden hairs," he said.

"It's a little thing to ask," thought I.
    "You're welcome enough to mine."
On the wood road dim, I gave them him.
    He smiled to see them shine.

He reached the fiddle from off his back,
    He threaded them one by one,
Brighter than golden wire they gleamed,
    Finer than silk new spun.

Then swift as shadow the thin bow flew.
    His fingers capered gay;
Birds, far and near, grew still to hear
    That elfin fiddler play.

And shy wood creatures with still bright gaze
    On soundless tread crept near,
The very leaves hung motionless
    Above my head to hear.

I could not feel my own heart beat,
    The breath died in my throat;
Stock still I stood in the shadowed wood,
    Lest I should miss one note.

Twilight came stealing from tree to tree,
    The little lights of town

Sprinkled the valley like buttercups,
   Or stars turned upside down;

And the fartherest one that I knew for mine,
   It would not let me stay;
Oh, the tune was sweet, but my town-weighed feet,
   They carried me away.

Carried me home to the valley lights,
   To the ticking clock on the stair,

To fire and cupboard and table spread
  With damask and willow ware.

So I laugh and gossip by candlelight
  To the clatter of plate and spoon,
But my cheeks turn hot for a secret spot
  And the lilt of a fairy tune.

And wherever I go and whatever I do
  Silvery, wild, and shrill,
I am hearing that little old man in green
  On the side of the humpbacked hill.

The neighbors may frown and shake their heads
  To see me stand and stare.
What should they know of fiddle bow
  And strings of golden hair?

Oh, I let them scold and I let them smile,
  And whisper of me apart,
For I have a hidden fairy tune
  In the bottom of my heart.

RACHEL FIELD

Flight of the Roller Coaster

Once more around should do it, the man confided . . .

and sure enough, when the roller coaster reached the peak
of the giant curve above me, screech of its wheels
almost drowned out by the shriller cries of the riders,

instead of the dip and plunge with its landslide of screams,
it rose in the air like a movieland magic carpet,

some wonderful bird,
and without fuss or fanfare swooped slowly across
    the amusement park,
over Spook's Castle, ice-cream booths, shooting gallery.
    And losing no height

made the last yards above the beach, where the cucumber-cool
brakeman in the last seat saluted
a lady about to change from her bathing suit.

Then, as many witnesses reported, headed leisurely
    out over the water,
disappearing all too soon behind a low-flying flight of clouds.

RAYMOND SOUSTER

The Wreck of the Julie Plante

On wan dark night on Lac St. Pierre,
    De win' she blow, blow, blow,
An' de crew of de wood-scow *Julie Plante*
    Got scairt an' run below—
For de win' she blow lak hurricane,
    Bimeby she blow some more,
An' de scow bust up on Lac St. Pierre
    Wan arpent* from de shore.

De captain walk on de front deck,
    An' walk de hin' deck too—
He call de crew from up de hole,
    He call de cook also.
De cook she's name was Rosie,
    She come from Montreal,
Was chambermaid on lumber barge
    On de Grande Lachine Canal.

* arpent: a French area unit equal to about one acre

De win' she blow from nor'-eas'-wes',
  De sout' win' she blow too,
When Rosie cry, "Mon cher captain,
  Mon cher, what I shall do?"
De captain t'row de beeg ankerre,
  But still de scow she dreef:
De crew he can't pass on de shore
  Becos' he los' hees skeef.

De night was dark lak wan black cat,
  De wave run high an' fas',
When de captain tak de Rosie girl
  An' tie her to de mas'.
Den he also tak de life-preserve,
  An' jomp off on de lak,
An' say, "Good-bye, my Rosie dear,
  I go drown for your sak!"

Nex' mornin' very early
  'Bout ha'f pas' two—t'ree—four—
De captain—scow—an' de poor Rosie
  Was corpses on de shore.
For de win' she blow lak hurricane,
  Bimeby she blow some more,
An' de scow bust up on Lac St. Pierre
  Wan arpent from de shore.

Now all good wood-scow sailorman,
  Tak warning by dat storm
An' go an' marry some nice French girl
  An' leev on wan beeg farm.
De win' can blow lak hurricane,
  An' s'pose she blow some more,
You can't get drown on Lac St. Pierre
  So long you stay on shore.

WILLIAM HENRY DRUMMOND

Legend

The blacksmith's boy went out with a rifle
and a black dog running behind.
Cobwebs snatched at his feet,
rivers hindered him,
thorn-branches caught at his eyes to make him blind
and the sky turned into an unlucky opal,
but he didn't mind.
I can break branches, I can swim rivers, I can stare out
    any spider I meet,
said he to his dog and his rifle.

The blacksmith's boy went over the paddocks
with his old black hat on his head.
Mountains jumped in his way,
rocks rolled down on him,
and the old crow cried, You'll soon be dead;
and the rain came down like mattocks.
But he only said
I can climb mountains, I can dodge rocks, I can shoot
    an old crow any day.
And he went on over the paddocks.

When he came to the end of the day the sun began falling.
Up came the night ready to swallow him,
like the barrel of a gun,
like an old black hat,
like a black dog hungry to follow him.
Then the pigeon, the magpie, and the dove began wailing,
and the grass lay down to pillow him.
His rifle broke, his hat blew away, and his dog was gone,
and the sun was falling.

But in front of the night the rainbow stood on the mountain
just as his heart foretold.

He ran like a hare,
he climbed like a fox,
he caught it in his hands, the colors and the cold—
like a bar of ice, like the columns of a fountain,
like a ring of gold.
The pigeon, the magpie, and the dove flew up to stare,
and the grass stood up again on the mountain.

The blacksmith's boy hung the rainbow on his shoulder,
instead of his broken gun.
Lizards ran out to see,
snakes made way for him,
and the rainbow shone as brightly as the sun.
All the world said, Nobody is braver, nobody is bolder,
nobody else has done
anything to equal it. He went home as easy as could be
with the swinging rainbow on his shoulder.

JUDITH WRIGHT

Love Stories

Castles and Candlelight

Castles and candlelight
Are courtly things.
Turreted high
For the children of Kings
Stands the fair castle
Over the strand,
And there with a candle
In her thin hand,
With tunes in her ears
And gold on her head
Climbs the sad Princess
Upstairs to bed.

Castles and candlelight
Are cruel things,
For castles have dungeons,
And moths have wings.
Woe to the shepherd boy
Who in darkness lies,
For viewing the Princess
With love in his eyes.
Ah, the poor shepherd boy—
How long will it be
Before the proud King
Will let him go free?

JAMES REEVES

Villikins and His Dinah

'Tis of a rich merchant who in London did dwell,
He had but one daughter, an unkimmon nice young gel;
Her name it was Dinah, scarce sixteen years old,
With a very large fortune in silver and gold.

As Dinah was a valiking in her gardin one day,
Her papa came up to her and thus he did say,
Go dress yourself Dinah in gorgeous array,
And take yourself a husiband both galliant and gay.

Oh, Papa, oh, Papa, I've not made up my mind,
For to get mar-ri-ed I don't feel inclined,
My very large fortune I'd gladly give o'er,
If I could remain single a year or two more.

Go, go, boldest daughter, the parient replied.
If you won't consent to be this here young man's bride,
I'll give your large fortune to the nearest of kin,
And you won't reap the benefit of one single pin.

As Villikins was a valiking in the garden around
He spied his dear Dinah lying dead upon the ground,
A cup of cold pison it lay by her side
With a billy-ducks* a-stating 'twas by pison she died.

He kissed her cold corpus a thousand times o'er,
And called her his dear Dinah though she was no more.
Then swallowed up the pison like a lovyer so brave,
And Villikins and his Dinah now lie buried in one grave.

---

* Billy-ducks: billet-doux (love letter)

[184]

Now all you young maidens take warning by her.
Never not by no means disobey your guv'ner,
And all you young gentlemen mind who you clap eyes on,
Think of Villikins and his Dinah and the cup of cold pison.

SAM COWELL

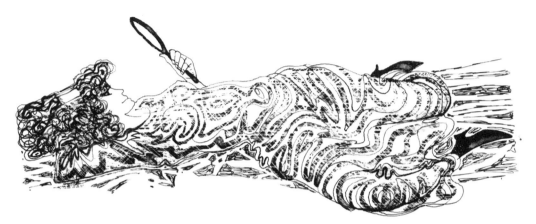

Intimates

Don't you care for my love? she said bitterly.

I handed her the mirror, and said:
Please address these questions to the proper person!
Please make all requests to headquarters!
In all matters of emotional importance
please approach the supreme authority direct!
So I handed her the mirror.

And she would have broken it over my head,
but she caught sight of her own reflection
and that held her spellbound for two seconds
while I fled.

D. H. LAWRENCE

The Modest Couple

When man and maiden meet, I like to see a drooping eye,
I always droop my own—I am the shyest of the shy.
I'm also fond of bashfulness, and sitting down on thorns,
For modesty's a quality that womankind adorns.

Whenever I am introduced to any pretty maid,
My knees they knock together, just as if I were afraid;
I flutter, and I stammer, and I turn a pleasing red,
For to laugh, and flirt, and ogle I consider most ill-bred.

But still in all these matters, as in other things below,
There is a proper medium, as I'm about to show.
I do not recommend a newly married pair to try
To carry on as Peter carried on with Sarah Bligh.

Betrothed they were when very young—before they'd learnt to
    speak
(For Sarah was but six days old, and Peter was a week);
Though little more than babies at those early ages, yet
They bashfully would faint when they occasionally met.

They blushed, and flushed, and fainted, till they reached the age
    of nine,
When Peter's good papa (he was a Baron of the Rhine)
Determined to endeavor some sound argument to find
To bring these shy young people to a proper frame of mind.

He told them that as Sarah was to be his Peter's bride,
They might at least consent to sit at table side by side;
He begged that they would now and then shake hands, till he was
    hoarse,
Which Sarah thought indelicate, and Peter very coarse.

And Peter in a tremble to the blushing maid would say,
"You must excuse Papa, Miss Bligh—it is his mountain way."
Says Sarah, "His behavior I'll endeavor to forget,
But your papa's the coarsest person that I ever met.

"He plighted us without our leave, when we were very young,
Before we had begun articulating with the tongue.
His underbred suggestions fill your Sarah with alarm;
Why, gracious me! he'll ask us next to walk out arm-in-arm!"

At length when Sarah reached the legal age of twenty-one,
The Baron he determined to unite her to his son;
And Sarah in a fainting fit for weeks unconscious lay,
And Peter blushed so hard you might have heard him miles away.

And when the time arrived for taking Sarah to his heart,
They were married in two churches half-a-dozen miles apart
(Intending to escape all public ridicule and chaff),
And the service was conducted by electric telegraph.

And when it was concluded, and the priest had said his say,
Until the time arrived when they were both to drive away,
They never spoke or offered for to fondle or to fawn,
For *he* waited in the attic, and *she* waited on the lawn.

At length, when four o'clock arrived, and it was time to go,
The carriage was announced, but decent Sarah answered "No!
Upon my word, I'd rather sleep my everlasting nap,
Than go and ride with Mr. Peter in a trap."

And Peter's oversensitive and highly polished mind
Wouldn't suffer him to sanction a proceeding of the kind;
And further, he declared he suffered overwhelming shocks
At the bare idea of having any coachman on the box.

So Peter into one turnout incontinently rushed,
While Sarah in a second trap sat modestly and blushed;
And Mr. Newman's coachman, on authority I've heard,
Drove away in gallant style upon the coach box of a third.

Now, though this modest couple in the matter of the car
Were very likely carrying a principle too far,
I hold their shy behavior was more laudable in them
Than that of Peter's brother with Miss Sarah's sister Em.

Alphonso, who in cool assurance all creation licks,
He up and said to Emmie (who had impudence for six),
"Miss Emily, I love you—will you marry? Say the word!"
And Emily said, "Certainly, Alphonso, like a bird!"

I do not recommend a newly married pair to try
To carry on as Peter carried on with Sarah Bligh,
But still their shy behavior was more laudable in them
Than that of Peter's brother with Miss Sarah's sister Em.

W. S. GILBERT

Kitty of Coleraine

As beautiful Kitty one morning was tripping
 With a pitcher of milk for the fair of Coleraine,
When she saw me she stumbled, the pitcher down tumbled,
 And all the sweet buttermilk watered the plain.
"Oh, what shall I do now? 'Twas looking at you now!
 I'm sure such a pitcher I'll ne'er see again.
'Twas the pride of my dairy. Oh, Barney McCleary,
 You're sent as a plague to the girls of Coleraine."

I sat down beside her, and gently did chide her
   That such a misfortune should give her such pain;
A kiss then I gave her, and before I did leave her
   She vowed for such pleasure she'd break it again.
'Twas the haymaking season—I can't tell the reason—
   Misfortunes will never come single, 'tis plain!
For very soon after poor Kitty's disaster
   The devil a pitcher was whole in Coleraine.

IRISH FOLK SONG

Lady Clare

It was the time when lilies blow
   And clouds are highest up in air;
Lord Ronald brought a lily-white doe
   To give his cousin, Lady Clare.

I trow they did not part in scorn:
   Lovers long-betrothed were they:
They two will wed the morrow morn:
   God's blessing on the day!

"He does not love me for my birth,
   Nor for my lands so broad and fair;
He loves me for my own true worth,
   And that is well," said Lady Clare.

In there came old Alice the nurse,
   Said: "Who was this that went from thee?"
"It was my cousin," said Lady Clare;
   "Tomorrow he weds with me."

"O God be thanked!" said Alice the nurse,
  "That all comes round so just and fair:
Lord Ronald is heir of all your lands,
  And you are not the Lady Clare."

"Are ye out of your mind, my nurse, my nurse,"
  Said Lady Clare, "that ye speak so wild?"
"As God's above," said Alice the nurse,
  "I speak the truth: you are my child.

"The old Earl's daughter died at my breast;
  I speak the truth, as I live by bread!
I buried her like my own sweet child,
  And put my child in her stead."

"Falsely, falsely have ye done,
  O Mother," she said, "if this be true,
To keep the best man under the sun
  So many years from his due."

"Nay now, my child," said Alice the nurse,
  "But keep the secret for your life,
And all you have will be Lord Ronald's
  When you are man and wife."

"If I'm a beggar born," she said,
  "I will speak out, for I dare not lie.
Pull off, pull off the brooch of gold,
  And fling the diamond necklace by."

"Nay now, my child," said Alice the nurse,
  "But keep the secret all ye can."
She said: "Not so: but I will know
  If there be any faith in man."

"Nay now, what faith?" said Alice the nurse,
  "The man will cleave unto his right."
"And he shall have it," the lady replied,
  "Though I should die tonight."

"Yet give one kiss to your mother dear!
  Alas, my child, I sinned for thee."
"O Mother, Mother, Mother," she said,
  "So strange it seems to me.

"Yet here's a kiss for my mother dear,
  My mother dear, if this be so,
And lay your hand upon my head,
  And bless me, Mother, ere I go."

She clad herself in a russet gown,
  She was no longer Lady Clare:
She went by dale, she went by down,
  With a single rose in her hair.

The lily-white doe Lord Ronald had brought
  Leapt up from where she lay,
Dropt her head in the maiden's hand,
  And follow'd her all the way.

Down stept Lord Ronald from his tower:
  "O Lady Clare, you shame your worth!
Why come you drest like a village maid,
  That are the flower of the earth?"

"If I come drest like a village maid,
  I am but as my fortunes are:
I am a beggar born," she said,
  "And not the Lady Clare."

"Play me no tricks," said Lord Ronald,
　"For I am yours in word and deed.
Play me no tricks," said Lord Ronald,
　"Your riddle is hard to read."

O and proudly stood she up!
　Her heart within her did not fail:
She looked into Lord Ronald's eyes,
　And told him all her nurse's tale.

He laughed a laugh of merry scorn:
　He turned and kissed her where she stood:
"If you are not the heiress born,
　And I," said he, "the next in blood—

"If you are not the heiress born,
　And I," said he, "the lawful heir,
We two will wed tomorrow morn,
　And you shall still be Lady Clare."

ALFRED, LORD TENNYSON

The Love-Talker

I met the Love-Talker one eve in the glen,
He was handsomer than any of our handsome young men,
His eyes were blacker than the sloe, his voice sweeter far
Than the crooning of old Kevin's pipes beyond in Coolnagar.

I was bound for the milking with a heart fair and free—
My grief! my grief! that bitter hour drained the life from me;
I thought him human lover, though his lips on mine were cold,
And the breath of death blew keen on me within his hold.

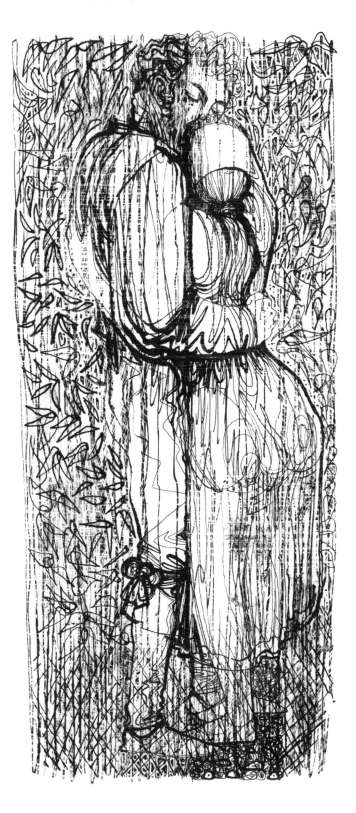

I know not what way he came, no shadow fell behind,
But all the sighing rushes swayed beneath a faery wind,
The thrush ceased its singing, a mist crept about,
We two clung together—with the world shut out.

Beyond the ghostly mist I could hear my cattle low,
The little cow from Ballina, clean as driven snow,
The dun cow from Kerry, the roan from Inisheer,
Oh, pitiful their calling—and his whispers in my ear!

His eyes were a fire; his words were a snare;
I cried my mother's name, but no help was there;
I made the blessed Sign; then he gave a dreary moan,
A wisp of cloud went floating by, and I stood alone.

Running ever through my head is an old-time rune—
"Who meets the Love-Talker must weave her shroud soon."
My mother's face is furrowed with the salt tears that fall,
But the kind eyes of my father are the saddest sight of all.

I have spun the fleecy lint, and now my wheel is still,
The linen length is woven for my shroud fine and chill,
I shall stretch me on the bed where a happy maid I lay—
Pray for the soul of Mare Og at dawning of the day!

ETHNA CARBERY

John-John

I dreamt last night of you, John-John,
    And thought you called to me;
And when I woke this morning, John,
    Yourself I hoped to see;
But I was all alone, John-John,
    Though still I heard your call;

I put my boots and bonnet on,
   And took my Sunday shawl,
And went, full sure to find you, John,
          At Nenagh fair.

The fair was just the same as then,
   Five years ago today,
When first you left the thimble men
   And came with me away;
For there again were thimble men
   And shooting galleries,
And card trick men and Maggie-men
   Of all sorts and degrees;
But not a sight of you, John-John,
          Was anywhere.

I turned my face to home again,
   And called myself a fool
To think you'd leave the thimble men
   And live again by rule,
And go to mass and keep the fast
   And till the little patch;
My wish to have you home was past
   Before I raised the latch
And pushed the door and saw you, John,
          Sitting down there.

How cool you came in here, begad,
   As if you owned the place!
But rest yourself there now, my lad,
   'Tis good to see your face;
My dream is out, and now by it
   I think I know my mind:
At six o'clock this house you'll quit,
   And leave no grief behind;—
But until six o'clock, John-John,
          My bit you'll share.

The neighbors' shame of me began
    When first I brought you in;
To wed and keep a tinker man
    They thought a kind of sin;
But now this three year since you're gone
    'Tis pity me they do,
And that I'd rather have, John-John,
    Than that they'd pity you,
Pity for me and you, John-John,
                I could not bear.

Oh, you're my husband right enough,
    But what's the good of that?
You know you never were the stuff
    To be the cottage cat,
To watch the fire and hear me lock
    The door and put out Shep—
But there, now, it is six o'clock
    And time for you to step.
God bless and keep you far, John-John!
                And that's my prayer.

THOMAS MACDONAGH

The Spinning Wheel

Mellow the moonlight to shine is beginning,
Close by the window young Eileen is spinning;
Bent over the fire her blind grandmother, sitting,
Is crooning, and moaning, and drowsily knitting:—
"Eileen, achora, I hear someone tapping."
" 'Tis the ivy, dear mother, against the glass flapping."
"Eily, I surely hear somebody sighing."
" 'Tis the sound, mother dear, of the summer wind dying."

Merrily, cheerily, noiselessly whirring,
Swings the wheel, spins the wheel, while the foot's stirring;
Sprightly, and brightly, and airily ringing
Thrills the sweet voice of the young maiden singing.

"What's that noise that I hear at the window, I wonder?"
" 'Tis the little birds chirping the holly-bush under."
"What makes you be shoving and moving your stool on,
And singing, all wrong, that old song of 'The Coolun'?"
There's a form at the casement—the form of her true love—
And he whispers, with face bent, "I'm waiting for you, love;
Get up on the stool, through the lattice step lightly,
We'll rove in the grove, while the moon's shining brightly."
Merrily, cheerily, noiselessly whirring,
Swings the wheel, spins the wheel, while the foot's stirring;
Sprightly, and brightly, and airily ringing
Thrills the sweet voice of the young maiden singing.

The maid shakes her head, on her lips lays her fingers,
Steals up from her seat—longs to go, and yet lingers;
A frightened glance turns to her drowsy grandmother,
Puts one foot on the stool, spins the wheel with the other,
Lazily, easily, swings now the wheel round,
Slowly and lowly is heard now the reel's sound;
Noiseless and light to the lattice above her
The maid steps—then leaps to the arms of her lover.
Slower—and slower—and slower the wheel swings;
Lower—and lower—and lower the reel rings;
Ere the reel and the wheel stopped their ringing and moving,
Through the grove the young lovers by moonlight are roving.

JOHN FRANCIS WALLER

Because I Were Shy

As I were a-walking upon a fine day,
I met a fine lady from over the way;
She smiled as she passed with a glint in her eye—
But I stood and I bloosh-ed because I were shy.

Says I to myself, "Come, Johnny," says I,
"If tha'd wish for to win her there's naught but to try."
So I doff-ed me 'at as I wink-ed me eye;
Then I donn-ed it on again 'cause I were shy.

She walk-ed before me for nearly a mile
Until she got stuck on the top of a stile.
Says she, "Willya 'elp me?" "I'll try it," says I;
But I 'ollered for Mother because I were shy.

She called me a noodle—I made a grimace,
Then she lifted her fist and she slapp-ed me face,
When up came me brother so spruce and so spry
And off I skedaddled because I were shy.

She 'ook-ed 'is arm, and she 'ook-ed 'im too;
They were wedded as soon as the banns 'ad gone through.
Now they've lots of wee childer and troubles foreby—
So I think I were lucky because I were shy.

ENGLISH FOLK SONG

The Man on the Flying Trapeze

Once I was happy, but now I'm forlorn,
Like an old coat, all tattered and torn,
Left in this wide world to fret and to mourn,
Betrayed by a wife in her teens.

Oh, the girl that I loved she was handsome,
I tried all I knew her to please,
But I could not please one quarter as well
As the man on the flying trapeze.

CHORUS:
He would fly through the air
With the greatest of ease,
This daring young man
On the flying trapeze;
His movements were graceful,
All girls he could please,
And my love he purloined away.

Her father and mother were both on my side,
And very hard tried to make her my bride.
Her father he sighed, and her mother she cried
To see her throw herself away.
'Twas all no avail, she'd go there every night
And throw him bouquets on the stage,
Which caused him to meet her; how he ran me down
To tell you would take a whole page.

One night I as usual called at her dear home,
Found there her father and mother alone.
I asked for my love, and soon they made known
To my horror that she'd run away.
She packed up her goods and eloped in the night
With him with the greatest of ease;
From three stories high he had lowered her down
To the ground on his flying trapeze.

Some months after this, I chanced in a hall,
Was greatly surprised to see on the wall
A bill in red letters that did my heart gall,
That she was appearing with him.
He taught her gymnastics and dressed her in tights
To help him to live at his ease,

And made her assume a masculine name,
And now she goes on the trapeze.

CHORUS:
She floats through the air
With the greatest of ease,
You'd think her a man
On the flying trapeze.
She does all the work
While he takes his ease,
And that's what became of my love.

ANONYMOUS

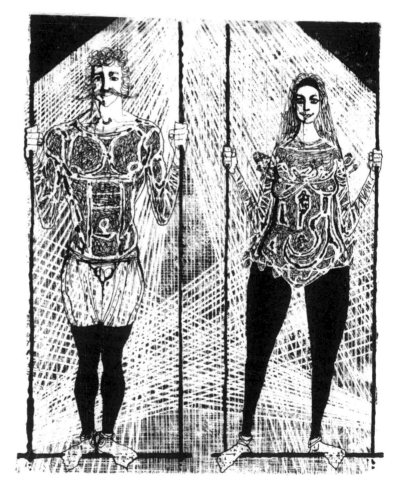

The Laird o' Cockpen

The laird o' Cockpen, he's proud an' he's great,
His mind is ta'en up wi' the things o' the state;
He wanted a wife his braw house to keep.
But favor wi' wooin' was fashious* to seek.

Doun by the dyke-side a lady did dwell,
At his table-head he thought she'd look well;
M'Cleish's ae daughter o' Claverse-ha Lee,
A penniless lass wi' a lang pedigree.

His wig was well pouther'd, and as guid as new,
His waistcoat was white, his coat it was blue,
He put on a ring, a sword, and cock'd hat—
And wha could refuse the laird wi' a' that?

He took the gray mare, and rade cannilie,
And rapp'd at the yett* o' Claverse-ha Lee:
"Gae tell Mistress Jean to come speedily ben,*
She's wanted to speak to the laird o' Cockpen."

Mistress Jean was makin' the elder-flower wine:
"And what brings the laird at sic a like time?"
She put off her apron and on her silk gown,
Her mutch wi' red ribbons, and gaed awa' doun.

And when she cam' ben, he bowed fu' low,
And what was his errand he soon let her know;
Amazed was the laird when the lady said "Na";
And wi' a laigh* curtsie she turned awa'.

---

* fashious: troublesome
* yett: gate
* ben: into the room
* laigh: low

Dumfounder'd he was, nae sigh did he gie,
He mounted his mare and he rade cannilie;
And often he thought, as he gaed thro' the glen,
She's daft to refuse the laird o' Cockpen.

LADY NAIRNE

The Whistling Thief

When Pat came o'er the hills his colleen for to see
His whistle low and shrill the signal was to be,
         (Shrill whistle)
Oh Mary, the mother said, someone is whistling sure,
Oh, Mother, it's only the wind that's whistling through the door.
        (Whistle "Garry Owen")

I've liv'd a long time, Mary, in this world, my dear,
But a door to whistle like that I never yet did hear.
But, Mother, you know the fiddle hangs close behind the sink,
And the wind upon the strings is playing that tune, I think.
          (Pig grunts)

Sure, Mary, I hear the pig uneasy in his mind.
But, Mother, you know they say that pigs can see the wind.
That's all very true in the day, but I think you may remark,
That pigs no more than we, can see anything in the dark
          (Dog barks)

The dog's barking now, and the fiddle can't play that tune,
But, Mother, you know that dogs will bark when they see the
  moon.
Now how can he see the moon, when you know the dog is blind?
Blind dogs can't bark at the moon, nor fiddles be played by the
  wind.

Now I am not such a fool as you think, I know very well it is Pat.
Shut your mouth, you whistling thief, and go along home out of
that;
Now you be off to your bed, and don't play before me your jeers,
For though I have lost my eyes, I have not yet lost my ears.

Now, chaps, when you go out and for your sweethearts wait,
Be sure you don't whistle too loud, or else the old woman you'll
wake;
In the days when they were young, forget they never can,
They are sure to tell the difference between a fiddle, a dog, or a
man.

IRISH SONG

Fighting Men

Lochinvar

O, young Lochinvar is come out of the west,
Through all the wide Border his steed was the best;
And save his good broadsword he weapons had none,
He rode all unarm'd and he rode all alone.
   So faithful in love and so dauntless in war,
    There never was knight like the young Lochinvar.

He staid not for brake, and he stopp'd not for stone,
He swam the Eske river where ford there was none;
But ere he alighted at Netherby gate,
The bride had consented; the gallant came late:
   For a laggard in love and a dastard in war
    Was to wed the fair Ellen of brave Lochinvar.

So boldly he enter'd the Netherby Hall,
Among bride's-men and kinsmen and brothers and all:
Then spoke the bride's father, his hand on his sword,
(For the poor craven bridegroom said never a word):
   "O come ye in peace here, or come ye in war,
    Or to dance at our bridal, young Lord Lochinvar?"

"I long woo'd your daughter, my suit you denied;
Love swells like the Solway, but ebbs like its tide—
And now am I come, with this lost love of mine,
To lead but one measure, drink one cup of wine.
   There are maidens in Scotland more lovely by far,
    That would gladly be bride to young Lochinvar."

The bride kiss'd the goblet: the knight took it up,
He quaff'd off the wine, and he threw down the cup.
She look'd down to blush and she look'd up to sigh,
With a smile on her lips, and a tear in her eye.

He took her soft hand ere her mother could bar,
"Now tread we a measure!" said young Lochinvar.

So stately his form, and so lovely her face,
That never a hall such a galliard did grace;
While her mother did fret, and her father did fume,
And the bridegroom stood dangling his bonnet and plume;
  And the bride-maidens whispered, " 'Twere better by far,
  To have matched our fair cousin with young Lochinvar."

One touch to her hand, and one word in her ear,
When they reach'd the hall door, and the charger stood near;
So light to the croupe the fair lady he swung,
So light to the saddle before her he sprung!
  "She is won! We are gone, over bank, bush, and scaur;
  They'll have fleet steeds that follow!" quoth young Lochinvar.

There was mounting 'mong Graemes of the Netherby clan;
Forsters, Fenwicks and Musgraves, they rode and they ran:
There was racing and chasing, on Cannobie Lee,
But the lost bride of Netherby ne'er did they see.
  So daring in love, and so dauntless in war,
  Have ye e'er heard of gallant like young Lochinvar?

SIR WALTER SCOTT

Jesse James

*(A DESIGN IN RED AND YELLOW
FOR A NICKEL LIBRARY)*

Jesse James was a two-gun man,
    (Roll on, Missouri!)
Strong-arm chief of an outlaw clan.
    (From Kansas to Illinois!)
He twirled an old Colt forty-five;
    (Roll on, Missouri!)

They never took Jesse James alive.
    (*Roll, Missouri, roll!*)
Jesse James was King of the Wes';
    (*Cataracts in the Missouri!*)
He'd a di'mon' heart in his lef' breas';
    (*Brown Missouri rolls!*)
He'd a fire in his heart no hurt could stifle:
    (*Thunder, Missouri!*)
Lion eyes an' a Winchester rifle.
    (*Missouri, roll down!*)

Jesse James rode a pinto hawse;
Come at night to a water-cawse;
Tetched with the rowel that pinto's flank;
She sprung the torrent from bank to bank.

Jesse rode through a sleepin' town;
Looked the moonlit street both up an' down;
Crack-crack-crack, the street ran flames
An' a great voice cried, "I'm Jesse James!"

Hawse an' afoot they're after Jess!
    (*Roll on, Missouri!*)
Spurrin' an' spurrin'—but he's gone Wes'.
    (*Brown Missouri rolls!*)
He was ten foot tall when he stood in his boots;
    (*Lightnin' like the Missouri!*)
More'n a match fer sich galoots.
    (*Roll, Missouri, roll!*)

Jesse James rode outa the sage;
Roun' the rocks come the swayin' stage;
Straddlin' the road a giant stan's
An' a great voice bellers, "Throw up yer han's!"

Jesse raked in the di'mon' rings,
The big gold watches an' the yuther things;
Jesse divvied 'em then an' thar
With a cryin' child had lost her mar.

The U.S. Troopers is after Jess;
    (*Roll on, Missouri!*)
Their hawses sweat foam, but he's gone Wes';
    (*Hear Missouri roar!*)
He was broad as a b'ar, he'd a ches' like a drum,
    (*Wind an' rain through Missouri!*)
An' his red hair flamed like Kingdom Come.
    (*Missouri down to the sea!*)

Jesse James all alone in the rain
Stopped an' stuck up the Eas'-boun' train;
Swayed through the coaches with horns an' a tail,
Lit out with the bullion an' the registered mail.

Jess made 'em all turn green with fright
Quakin' in the aisles in the pitch-black night;
An' he give all the bullion to a poor ole tramp
Campin' nigh the cuttin' in the dirt an' damp.

The whole U.S. is after Jess;
    (*Roll on, Missouri!*)
The son-of-a-gun, if he ain't gone Wes';
    (*Missouri to the sea!*)
He could chaw gold iron an' spit blue flame;
    (*Cataracts down the Missouri!*)
He rode on a catamount he'd larned to tame.
    (*Hear that Missouri roll!*)

Jesse James rode into a bank;
Give his pinto a tetch on the flank;
Jumped the teller's window with an awful crash;
Heaved up the safe an' twirled his moustache;

He said, "So long, boys!" He yelped, "So long!
Feelin' porely today—I ain't feelin' strong!"
Rode right through the wall a-goin' crack-crack-crack—
Took the safe home to mother in a gunnysack.

They're creepin'; they're crawlin', they're stalkin' Jess;
    (Roll on, Missouri!)
They's a rumor he's gone much further Wes';
    (Roll, Missouri, roll!)
They's word of a cayuse hitched to the bars
    (Ruddy clouds on Missouri!)
Of a golden sunset that busts into stars.
    (Missouri, roll down!)

Jesse James rode hell fer leather;
He was a hawse an' a man together;
In a cave in a mountain high up in air
He lived with a rattlesnake, a wolf, an' a bear.

Jesse's heart was as sof' as a woman;
Fer guts an' stren'th he was sooper-human;
He could put six shots through a woodpecker's eye
And take in one swaller a gallon o' rye.

They sought him here an' they sought him there,
    (Roll on, Missouri!)
But he strides by night through the ways of the air;
    (Brown Missouri rolls!)
They say he was took an' they say he is dead,
    (Thunder, Missouri!)
But he ain't—he's a sunset overhead!
    (Missouri down to the sea!)

Jesse James was a Hercules.
When he went through the woods he tore up the trees.
When he went on the plains he smoked the groun'
An' the hull lan' shuddered fer miles aroun'.

Jesse James wore a red bandanner
That waved on the breeze like the Star Spangled Banner;
In seven states he cut up dadoes.
He's gone with the buffler an' the desperadoes.

Yes, Jesse James was a two-gun man
    (Roll on, Missouri!)
The same as when this song began;
    (From Kansas to Illinois!)
An' when you see a sunset bust into flames
    (Lightnin' like the Missouri!)
Or a thunderstorm blaze—that's Jesse James!
    (Hear that Missouri roll!)

WILLIAM ROSE BENÉT

The Tarry Buccaneer

I'm going to be a pirate with a bright brass pivot-gun,
And an island in the Spanish Main beyond the setting sun,
And a silver flagon full of red wine to drink when work is done,
    Like a fine old salt-sea scavenger, like a tarry buccaneer.

With a sandy creek to careen in, and a pigtailed Spanish mate,
And under my main hatches a sparkling merry freight
Of doubloons and double moidores and pieces of eight,
    Like a fine old salt-sea scavenger, like a tarry buccaneer.

With a taste for Spanish wineshops and for spending my
    doubloons,
And a crew of swart mulattoes and black-eyed octoroons,
And a thoughtful way with mutineers of making them maroons,
    Like a fine old salt-sea scavenger, like a tarry buccaneer.

With a sash of crimson velvet and a diamond-hilted sword,
And a silver whistle about my neck secured to a golden cord,
And a habit of taking captives and walking them along a board,
    Like a fine old salt-sea scavenger, like a tarry buccaneer.

With a spyglass tucked beneath my arm and a cocked hat cocked
    askew,

And a long low rakish schooner a-cutting of the waves in two,
And a flag of skull and crossbones the wickedest that ever flew,
Like a fine old salt-sea scavenger, like a tarry buccaneer.

JOHN MASEFIELD

The Death of Ben Hall

Ben Hall was out on the Lachlan side
With a thousand pounds on his head;
A score of troopers were scattered wide
And a hundred more were ready to ride
Wherever a rumor led.

They had followed his track from the Weddin heights
And north by the Weelong yards;
Through dazzling days and moonlit nights
They had sought him over their rifle sights,
With their hands on their trigger guards.

The outlaw stole like a hunted fox
Through the scrub and stunted heath,
And peered like a hawk from his eyrie rocks
Through the waving boughs of the sapling box
On the troopers riding beneath.

His clothes were rent by the clutching thorn
And his blistered feet were bare;
Ragged and torn, with his beard unshorn,
He hid in the woods like a beast forlorn,
With a padded path to his lair.

But every night when the white stars rose
He crossed by the Gunning Plain
To a stockman's hut where the Gunning flows,

And struck on the door three swift light blows,
And a hand unhooked the chain—

And the outlaw followed the lone path back
With food for another day;
And the kindly darkness covered his track
And the shadows swallowed him deep and black
Where the starlight melted away.

But his friend had read of the Big Reward,
And his soul was stirred with greed;
He fastened his door and window-board,
He saddled his horse and crossed the ford,
And spurred to the town at speed.

You may ride at a man's or a maid's behest
When honor or true love call
And steel your heart to the worst or best,
But the ride that is ta'en on a traitor's quest
Is the bitterest ride of all.

A hot wind blew from the Lachlan bank
And a curse on its shoulder came;
The pine trees frowned at him, rank on rank,
The sun on a gathering storm-cloud sank
And flushed his cheek with shame.

He reined at the Court; and the tale began
That the rifles alone should end;
Sergeant and trooper laid their plan
To draw the net on a hunted man
At the treacherous word of a friend.

False was the hand that raised the chain
And false was the whispered word:
"The troopers have turned to the south again,
You may dare to camp on the Gunning Plain."
And the weary outlaw heard.

He walked from the hut but a quarter-mile
Where a clump of sapling stood
In a sea of grass like a lonely isle;
And the moon came up in a little while
Like silver steeped in blood.

Ben Hall lay down on the dew-wet ground
By the side of his tiny fire;
And a night-breeze woke, and he heard no sound
As the troopers drew their cordon round—
And the traitor earned his hire.

And nothing they saw in the dim gray light,
But the little glow in the trees;
And they crouched in the tall cold grass all night,
Each one ready to shoot at sight,
With his rifle cocked on his knees.

When the shadows broke and the dawn's white sword
Swung over the mountain wall,
And a little wind blew over the ford,
A sergeant sprang to his feet and roared:
"In the name of the Queen, Ben Hall!"

Haggard, the outlaw leapt from his bed
With his lean arms held on high.
"Fire!" And the word was scarcely said
When the mountains rang to a rain of lead—
And the dawn went drifting by.

They kept their word and they paid his pay
Where a clean man's hand would shrink;
And that was the traitor's master-day
As he stood by the bar on his homeward way
And called on the crowd to drink.

He banned no creed and he barred no class,
And he called to his friends by name;

But the worst would shake his head and pass
And none would drink from the bloodstained glass
And the goblet red with shame.

And I know when I hear the last grim call
And my mortal hour is spent,
When the light is hid and the curtains fall
I would rather sleep with the dead Ben Hall
Than go where that traitor went.

WILL H. OGILVIE

Brady's Bend

This is the story of
The brawny Brady riflemen,
John,
     James,
And the celebrated Samuel—
Who fought Bald Eagle with
The Pennsylvania rifle when
Chief Bald Eagle was
The tomahawk of hell.

Old John Brady was
At Valley Forge and Germantown,
Some
     say,
At the battle of the Brandywine.
He brought a many of
The tomahawking vermin down,
Before they fixed him with
The Indian sign.

Young Jim Brady was
A-harvesting a field in ear,

Long
    gun
Left a-leaning on a stubble stack,
When Chief Bald Eagle like
A weasel come a-eeling near,
And dropped Jim Brady with
A bullet in his back.

Left him lying like
A chicken when its head is chopped,
Scalped
    him
With a whooping-coughing caterwaul.
But sure and as soon as
The shooting and the shouting stopped,
The dead man dying there
Begun to crawl.

Crawled to the riverbank
A-hunting for a boat he had
Hid
    there,
Half rotting in the river mud.
For help was afar away,
And forty mile to float he had,
Young Jim Brady with
His head all over blood.

Down the Susquehanna he
Slipped across the river sand,
Wet
    rock
A-shining like a scalping knife.
Sunset, sunrise
Burned upon the river and
Reddened, like his forehead with
The blood of life.

"Tell my brother how
Bald Eagle took my hair away.
Tell
     Sam
To remember, like I told him, to
Trail Bald Eagle like
A beagle over there away,
And lift the scalping lock
The Indians do."

Up the Allegheny where
The Great Chief made his stand,
Sam
          went
A-harrying and hunting him.
Till back by the river bend,
That's named now for Brady's band,
He scalped Bald Eagle like
He promised Jim.

He killed Bald Eagle by
The river Allegheny—a
Great
          Chief—
Did the Samuel, aforesaid,
Who scalped more Indians in
The State of Pennsylvania
Than any other white man
Alive or dead.

This is the story of
The brawny Brady riflemen,
  John,
     James,
And the celebrated Samuel—
Who fought Bald Eagle with
The Pennsylvania rifle when

Chief Bald Eagle was
The tomahawk of hell.

MARTHA KELLER

The War Song of Dinas Vawr

The mountain sheep are sweeter,
But the valley sheep are fatter;
We therefore deemed it meeter
To carry off the latter.
We made an expedition;
We met a host, and quelled it;
We forced a strong position,
And killed the men who held it.

On Dyfed's richest valley,
Where herds of kine were browsing,
We made a mighty sally,
To furnish our carousing,
Fierce warriors rushed to meet us;
We met them, and o'erthrew them:
They struggled hard to beat us;
But we conquered them, and slew them.

As we drove our prize at leisure,
The king marched forth to catch us:
His rage surpassed all measure,
But his people could not match us.
He fled to his hall pillars;
And, ere our force we led off,
Some sacked his house and cellars,
While others cut his head off.

We there, in strife bewild'ring,
Spilt blood enough to swim in:
We orphaned many children,
And widowed many women.
The eagles and the ravens
We glutted with our foemen;
The heroes and the cravens,
The spearmen and the bowmen.

We brought away from battle,
And much their land bemoaned them,
Two thousand head of cattle,
And the head of him who owned them:
Ednyfed, king of Dyfed,
His head was borne before us;
His wine and beasts supplied our feasts,
And his overthrow, our chorus.

THOMAS LOVE PEACOCK

The Relief of Lucknow

Oh, that last day in Lucknow fort!
    We knew that it was the last;
That the enemy's lines crept surely in,
    And the end was coming fast.

To yield to that foe meant worse than death;
    And the men and we all worked on;
It was one day more of smoke and roar,
    And then it would all be done.

There was one of us, a corporal's wife,
    A fair, young gentle thing,

Wasted with fever in the siege,
   And her mind was wandering.

She lay on the ground, in her Scottish plaid,
   And I took her head on my knee;
"When my father comes hame frae the pleugh," she said,
   "Oh! then please wauken me."

She slept like a child on her father's floor,
   In the flecking of woodbine shade,
When the house dog sprawls by the open door,
   And the mother's wheel is stayed.

It was smoke and roar and powder stench,
   And hopeless waiting for death;
And the soldier's wife, like a full-tired child,
   Seemed scarce to draw her breath.

I sank to sleep; and I had my dream
   Of an English village lane,
And wall and garden;—but one wild scream
   Brought me back to the roar again.

There Jessie Brown stood listening
   And then a broad gladness broke
All over her face, and she took my hand
   And drew me near and spoke:

"The Hielanders! O! dinna ye hear
   The slogan far awa'?
The McGregor's? O! I ken it weel;
   It's the grandest o' them a'!

"God bless the bonny Hielanders!
   We're saved! we're saved!" she cried;
And fell on her knees; and thanks to God
   Flowed forth like a full flood tide.

Along the battery line her cry
    Had fallen among the men,
And they started back, for they were there to die;
    But was life so near them, then?

They listened for life; and the rattling fire
    Far off, and the far-off roar,
Were all; and the colonel shook his head,
    And they turned to their guns once more.

Then Jessie said, "The slogan's done;
    Can ye no hear it, noo,
'The Campbells are comin' '? It's no a dream;
    Our succors hae broken through!"

We heard the roar and the rattle afar,
    But the pipes we could not hear;
So the men plied their work of hopeless war,
    And knew that the end was near.

It was not long ere it must be heard—
    A shrilling, ceaseless sound:
It was no noise from the strife afar,
    Or the sappers underground.

It *was* the pipes of the Highlanders!
    And now they played "Auld Lang Syne":
It came to our men like the voice of God,
    And they shouted along the line.

And they wept, and shook one another's hands,
    And the women sobbed in a crowd;
And everyone knelt down where he stood,
    And we all thanked God aloud.

That happy time, when we welcomed them,
    Our men put Jessie first;

And the general gave her his hand, and cheers
   From the men, like a volley burst.

And the pipers' ribbons and tartans streamed,
   Marching round and round our line;
And our joyful cheers were broken with tears,
   As the pipes played "Auld Lang Syne."

ROBERT SPENCE TRAILL LOWELL

How Robin Hood Rescued the Widow's Sons

There are twelve months in all the year,
   As I hear many say,
But the merriest month in all the year
   Is the merry month of May.

Now Robin Hood is to Nottingham gone,
   With a link a down and a day,
And there he met a silly old woman,
   Was weeping on the way.

"What news? What news, thou silly old woman?
   What news hast thou for me?"
Said she, "There's my three sons in Nottingham town
   Today condemned to die."

"O, have they parishes burnt?" he said,
   "Or have they ministers slain?
Or have they robbed any virgin,
   Or other men's wives have ta'en?"

"They have no parishes burnt, good sir,
   Nor yet have ministers slain,

Nor have they robbed any virgin,
  Nor other men's wives have ta'en."

"O, what have they done?" said bold Robin Hood,
  "I pray thee tell to me."
"It's for slaying of the king's fallow deer,
  Bearing their long bows with thee."

"Dost thou not mind, old woman," he said,
  "How thou mad'st me to sup and dine?
By the truth of my body," quoth bold Robin Hood,
  "You could not tell it in better time."

Now Robin Hood is to Nottingham gone,
  With a link a down and a day,
And there he met with a silly old palmer,
  Was walking along the highway.

"What news? What news, thou silly old man?
  What news, I do thee pray?"
Said he, "Three squires in Nottingham town
  Are condemned to die this day."

"Come change thy apparel with me, old man,
  Come change thy apparel for mine;
Here is ten shillings in good silver;
  Go drink it in beer or wine."

"O, thine apparel is good," he said,
  "And mine is ragged and torn;
Wherever you go, wherever you ride,
  Laugh not an old man to scorn."

"Come change thy apparel with me, old churl,
  Come change thy apparel with mine;
Here is a piece of good broad gold;
  Go feast thy brethren with wine."

Then he put on the old man's hat,
    It stood full high on the crown:
"The first bold bargain that I come at,
    It shall make thee come down!"

Then he put on the old man's cloak,
    Was patched black, blue, and red;
He thought it no shame, all the day long,
    To wear the bags of bread.

Then he put on the old man's breeks,
    Was patched from leg to side:
"By the truth of my body," bold Robin can say,
    "This man loved little pride!"

Then he put on the old man's hose,
    Were patched from knee to wrist:
"By the truth of my body," said bold Robin Hood,
    "I'd laugh if I had any list."

Then he put on the old man's shoes,
    Were patched both beneath and aboon:
Then Robin Hood swore a solemn oath,
    "It's good habit that make a man."

Now Robin Hood is to Nottingham gone,
    With a link a down and a down,
And there he met with the proud sheriff,
    Was walking along the town.

"Save you, save you, Sheriff!" he said.
    "Now heaven you save and see!
And what will you give to a silly old man
    Today will your hangman be?"

"Some suits, some suits," the sheriff he said,
    "Some suits I'll give to thee;

Some suits, some suits, and pence thirteen,
    Today's a hangman's fee."

Then Robin he turns him round about,
    And jumps from stock to stone:
"By the truth of my body," the sheriff he said,
    "That's well jumpt, thou nimble old man!"

"I was ne'er a hangman in all my life,
    Nor yet intends to trade:
But curst be he," said bold Robin,
    "That first was a hangman made!

"I've a bag for meal, and a bag for malt,
    And a bag for barley and corn;
A bag for bread, and a bag for beef,
    And a bag for my little small horn.

"I have a horn in my pocket,
    I got it from Robin Hood,
And still when I set it to my mouth,
    For thee it blows little good."

"O, wind thy horn, thou proud fellow!
    Of thee I have no doubt.
I wish that thou give such a blast,
    Till both thy eyes fall out."

The first loud blast that he did blow
    He blew both loud and shrill;
A hundred and fify of Robin Hood's men
    Came riding over the hill.

The next loud blast that he did give
    He blew both loud and amain,
And quickly sixty of Robin Hood's men
    Came shining over the plain.

"O, who are those," the sheriff he said,
  "Come tripping over the lea?"
"They're my attendants," brave Robin did say;
  "They'll pay a visit to thee."

They took the gallows from the slack,
  They set it in the glen,
They hanged the proud sheriff on that,
  And released their own three men.

OLD ENGLISH BALLAD

The Highwayman's Ghost

Twelve o'clock—a misty night—
Glimpsing hints of buried light—
Six years strung in an iron chain—
Time I stood on the ground again!

So—by your leave! Slip, easy enough,
Withered wrists from the rusty cuff.
The old chain rattles, the old wood groans,
O the clatter of clacking bones!

Here I am, uncoated, unhatted,
Shirt all mildewed, hair all matted,
Sockets that each have royally
Fed the crow with a precious eye.

O for slashing Bess the brown!
Where, old lass, have they earthed thee down?
Sobb'st beneath a carrier's throng?
Strain'st a coalman's cart along?

Shame to foot it!—must be so.
See, the mists are smitten below;
Over the moorland, wide away,
Moonshine pours her watery day.

There the long white-dusted track,
There a crawling speck of black.
The Northern mail, ha ha! and he
There on the box is Anthony.

Coachman I scared him from brown to gray,
Witness he lied my blood away.
Haste, Fred! haste, boy! never fail!
Now or never! catch the mail!

The horses plunge, and sweating stop.
Dead falls Tony, neck and crop.
Nay, good guard, small profit thus,
Shooting ghosts with a blunderbuss!

Crash wheel! coach over! How it rains
Hampers, ladies, wigs, and canes!
O the spoil! to sack it and lock it!
But, woe is me, I have never a pocket!

RICHARD GARNETT

The Knight's Leap

A LEGEND OF ALTENAHR

So the foemen have fired the gate, men of mine;
    And the water is spent and gone?
Then bring me a cup of the red Ahr-wine:
    I never shall drink but this one.

And reach me my harness, and saddle my horse,
    And lead him me round to the door:
He must take such a leap tonight perforce,
    As horse never took before.

I have fought my fight, I have lived my life,
    I have drunk my share of wine;
From Trier to Coln there was never a knight
    Led a merrier life than mine.

I have lived by the saddle for years two score;
    And if I must die on tree,
Then the old saddletree, which has borne me of yore,
    Is the properest timber for me.

So now to show bishop, and burgher, and priest,
    How the Altenahr hawk can die:
If they smoke the old falcon out of his nest,
    He must take to his wings and fly!

He harnessed himself by the clear moonshine,
    And he mounted his horse at the door;
And he drained such a cup of the red Ahr-wine,
    As man never drained before.

He spurred the old horse, and he held him tight,
    And he leapt him out over the wall;
Out over the cliff, out into the night,
    Three hundred feet of fall.

They found him next morning below in the glen,
    With never a bone in him whole—
A mass or a prayer, now, good gentlemen,
    For such a bold rider's soul.

CHARLES KINGSLEY

Allen-a-Dale

Allen-a-Dale has no fagot for burning,
Allen-a-Dale has no furrow for turning,
Allen-a-Dale has no fleece for the spinning,
Yet Allen-a-Dale has red gold for the winning.
Come, read me my riddle! come, hearken my tale!
And tell me the craft of bold Allen-a-Dale.

The Baron of Ravensworth prances in pride,
And he views his domains upon Arkindale side.
The mere for his net, and the land for his game,
The chase for the wild, and the park for the tame;

Yet the fish of the lake, and the deer of the vale
Are less free to Lord Dacre than Allen-a-Dale!

Allen-a-Dale was ne'er belted a knight,
Though his spur be as sharp, and his blade be as bright;
Allen-a-Dale is no baron or lord,
Yet twenty tall yeomen will draw at his word;
And the best of our nobles his bonnet will vail,
Who at Rere-cross on Stanmore meets Allen-a-Dale.

Allen-a-Dale to his wooing is come;
The mother, she asked of his household and home:
"Though the castle of Richmond stand fair on the hill,
My hall," quoth bold Allen, "shows gallanter still;
'Tis the blue vault of heaven, with its crescent so pale,
And with all its bright spangles!" said Allen-a-Dale.

The father was steel, and the mother was stone;
They lifted the latch, and they bade him be gone;
But loud, on the morrow, their wail and their cry:
He had laughed on the lass with his bonny black eye,
And she fled to the forest to hear a love tale,
And the youth it was told by was Allen-a-Dale!

SIR WALTER SCOTT

The Old Man and Jim

Old man never had much to say—
    'Ceptin' to Jim,
And Jim was the wildest boy he had—
    And the old man jes' wrapped up in him!
Never heerd him speak but once
Er twice in my life,—and first time was
When the army broke out, and Jim he went,

The old man backin' him, fer three months;
And all 'at I heerd the old man say
Was, jes' as we turned to start away—
  "Well, good-by, Jim:
    Take keer of yourse'f!"

'Peared-like, he was more satisfied
  Jes' *lookin'* at Jim
And likin' him all to hisse'f-like, see?—
  'Cause he was jes' wrapped up in him!
And over and over I mind the day
The old man come and stood round in the way
While we was drillin', a-watchin' Jim—
And down at the deepo a-heern' him say,
  "Well, good-by, Jim:
    Take keer of yourse'f!"

Never was nothin' about the *farm*
  Disting'ished Jim;
Neighbors all ust to wonder why
  The old man 'peared wrapped up in him:
But when Capt. Biggler he writ back
'At Jim was the bravest boy we had
In the whole dern rigiment, white er black,
And his fightin' good as his farmin' bad—
'At he had led, with a bullet clean
Bored through his thigh, and carried the flag
Through the bloodiest battle you ever seen—
The old man wound up a letter to him
'At Cap. read to us, 'at said: "Tell Jim
  Good-by
    And take keer of hisse'f!"

Jim come home jes' long enough
  To take the whim
'At he'd like to go back in the cavelry—
  And the old man jes' wrapped up in him!

Jim 'lowed 'at he'd had sich luck afore,
Guessed he'd tackle her three years more.
And the old man give him a colt he'd raised,
And follered him over to Camp Ben Wade,
And laid eround for a week er so,
Watchin' Jim on dress parade;
'Tel finally he rid away,
And last he heered was the old man say--
    "Well, good-by, Jim:
        Take keer of yourse'f!"

Tuk the papers, the old man did,
    A-watchin' fer Jim,
Fully believin' he'd make his mark
    Some way—jes' wrapped up in him!
And many a time the word 'ud come
'At stirred him up like the tap of a drum.
At Petersburg, fer instunce, where
Jim rid right into their cannons there,
And tuk 'em, and p'inted 'em t'other way
And socked it home to the boys in gray,
As they skooted fer timber, and on and on—
Jim a lieutenant,—and one arm gone—
And the old man's words in his mind all day—
    "Well, good-by, Jim:
        Take keer of yourse'f!"

Think of a private, now, perhaps,
    We'll say like Jim,
'At's clumb clean up to the shoulder straps—
    And the old man jes' wrapped up in him!
Think of him—with the war plum' through,
And the glorious old Red-White-and-Blue
A-laughin' the news down over Jim,
And the old man, bendin' over him—
The surgeon turnin' away with tears
'At hadn't leaked fer years and years,

As the hand of the dyin' boy clung to
His father's, the old voice in his ears,—
      "Well, good-by, Jim:
          Take keer of yourse'f!"

JAMES WHITCOMB RILEY

Disabled

He sat in a wheeled chair, waiting for dark,
And shivered in his ghastly suit of gray,
Legless, sewn short at elbow. Through the park
Voices of boys rang saddening like a hymn,
Voices of play and pleasure after day,
Till gathering sleep had mothered them from him.

About this time Town used to swing so gay
When glow lamps budded in the light blue trees,
And girls glanced lovelier as the air grew dim,—
In the old times, before he threw away his knees.
Now he will never feel again how slim
Girls' waists are, or how warm their subtle hands;
All of them touch him like some queer disease.

There was an artist silly for his face,
For it was younger than his youth, last year.
Now, he is old; his back will never brace;
He's lost his color very far from here,
Poured it down shell holes till the veins ran dry,
And half his lifetime lapsed in the hot race,
And leap of purple spurted from his thigh.

One time he liked a blood-smear down his leg,
After the matches, carried shoulder-high.

It was after football, when he'd drunk a peg,
He thought he'd better join.—He wonders why.
Someone had said he'd look a god in kilts,
That's why; and maybe, too, to please his Meg;
Aye, that was it, to please the giddy jilts
He asked to join. He didn't have to beg;
Smiling they wrote his lie; aged nineteen years.
Germans he scarcely thought of; all their guilt,
And Austria's, did not move him. And no fears
Of Fear came yet. He thought of jeweled hilts
For daggers in plaid socks; of smart salutes;
And care of arms; and leave; and pay arrears;
Esprit de corps, and hints for young recruits.
And soon he was drafted out with drums and cheers.

Some cheered him home, but not as crowds cheer Goal.
Only a solemn man who brought him fruits
Thanked him; and then inquired about his soul.

Now, he will spend a few sick years in Institutes,
And do what things the rules consider wise,

And take whatever pity they may dole.
Tonight he noticed how the women's eyes
Passed from him to the strong men that were whole.
How cold and late it is! Why don't they come
And put him into bed? Why don't they come?

WILFRED OWEN

The Three Songs

King Siegfried sat in his lofty hall:
"Ye harpers! who sings the best song of all?"
Then a youth stepped forth with a scornful lip,
The harp in his hand, and the sword at his hip.

"Three songs I know; but this first song
Thou, O King! hast forgotten long:
Thou hast stabbed my brother with murderous hand—
Hast stabbed my brother with murderous hand!

"The second song I learned aright
In the midst of a dark and stormy night:
Thou must fight with me for life or death—
Must fight with me for life or death!"

On the banquet table he laid his harp,
And they both drew out their swords so sharp;
And they fought in the sight of the harpers all,
Till the King sank dead in the lofty hall.

"And now for the third, the proudest, best!
I shall sing it, sing it, and never rest:
King Siegfried lies in his red, red blood—
Siegfried lies in his red, red blood!"

BAYARD TAYLOR

Waltzing Matilda

Once a jolly swagman* camped by a billabong*
Under the shade of a coolibah tree.
And he sang as he watched and waited till his billy* boiled:
"You'll come a-waltzing, Matilda, with me!"

CHORUS:
Waltzing, Matilda, waltzing, Matilda,
You'll come a-waltzing, Matilda, with me.
And he sang as he watched and waited till his billy boiled,
"You'll come a-waltzing, Matilda, with me!"

Down came a jumbuck* to drink at the billabong,
Up jumped the swagman and grabbed him with glee,
And he sang as he stowed that jumbuck in his tucker-bag:
"You'll come a-waltzing, Matilda, with me!"

CHORUS:
Waltzing, Matilda, waltzing, Matilda,
You'll come a-waltzing, Matilda, with me.
And he sang as he stowed that jumbuck in his tucker-bag:
"You'll come a-waltzing, Matilda, with me!"

Up rode the squatter* mounted on his thoroughbred,
Down came the troopers, one, two, three,
And his, "Where's that jolly jumbuck you've got in your tucker-
    bag?"
"You'll come a-waltzing, Matilda, with me!"

CHORUS:
Waltzing, Matilda, waltzing, Matilda,

---

* swagman: tramp
* billabong: mudhole
* billy: tin for food or liquid
* jumpbuck: sheep
* squatter: sheep farmer

You'll come a-waltzing, Matilda, with me.
And his, "Where's that jolly jumbuck you've got in your tucker-
    bag?"
"You'll come a-waltzing, Matilda, with me!"

Up jumped the swagman, sprang into the billabong.
"You'll never catch me alive," said he.
And his ghost may be heard as you pass by that billabong:
"You'll come a-waltzing, Matilda, with me!"

CHORUS:
Waltzing, Matilda, waltzing, Matilda,
You'll come a-waltzing, Matilda, with me.
And his ghost may be heard as you pass by that billabong:
"You'll come a-waltzing, Matilda, with me!"

AUSTRALIAN FOLK SONG

The Death of Robin Hood

"Give me my bow," said Robin Hood,
    "An arrow give to me;
And when 'tis shot mark thou that spot,
    For there my grave shall be."

Then Little John did make no sign,
    And not a word he spake;
But he smiled, altho' with mickle woe
    His heart was like to break.

He raised his master in his arms,
    And set him on his knee;
And Robin's eyes beheld the skies,
    The shaws, the greenwood tree.

The brook was babbling as of old,
  The birds sang full and clear.
And the wild flowers gay like a carpet lay
  In the path of the timid deer.

"O Little John," said Robin Hood,
  "Meseemeth now to be
Standing with you so stanch and true
  Under the greenwood tree.

"And all around I hear the sound
  Of Sherwood long ago,
And my merry men come back again—
  You know, sweet friend, you know!

"Now mark this arrow; where it falls,
  When I am dead dig deep,
And bury me there in the greenwood where
  I would forever sleep."

He twanged his bow. Upon its course
  The clothyard arrow sped,
And when it fell in yonder dell,
  Brave Robin Hood was dead.

The sheriff sleeps in a marble vault,
  The king in a shroud of gold;
And upon the air with a chanted pray'r
  Mingles the mock of mold.

But the deer draw to the shady pool,
  The birds sing blithe and free,
And the wild flow'rs bloom o'er a hidden tomb
  Under the greenwood tree.

EUGENE FIELD

The Spelling Bee at Angels

(REPORTED BY TRUTHFUL JAMES)

Waltz in, waltz in, ye little kids, and gather round my knee,
And drop them books and first pothooks, and hear a yarn from
   me.
I kin not sling a fairy tale of Jinnys fierce and wild,
For I hold it is unchristian to deceive a simple child;
But as from school yer driftin' by, I thowt ye'd like to hear
Of a "Spelling Bee" at Angels that we organized last year.

It warn't made up of gentle kids, of pretty kids, like you,
But gents ez hed their reg'lar growth, and some enough for two.
There woz Lanky Jim of Sutter's Fork and Bilson of Lagrange,
And "Pistol Bob," who wore that day a knife by way of change.
You start, you little kids, you think these are not pretty names,
But each had a man behind it, and—my name is Truthful James.

There was Poker Dick from Whisky Flat, and Smith of Shooter's
   Bend,
And Brown of Calaveras—which I want no better friend;
Three-fingered Jack—yes, pretty dears, three fingers—*you* have five.
Clapp cut off two—it's sing'lar, too, that Clapp ain't now alive.
'Twas very wrong indeed, my dears, and Clapp was much to
   blame;
Likewise was Jack, in afteryears, for shootin' of that same.

The nights was kinder lengthenin' out, the rains had jest begun,
When all the camp came up to Pete's to have their usual fun;
But we all sot kinder sad-like around the barroom stove
Till Smith got up, permiskiss-like, and this remark he hove:
"Thar's a new game down in Frisco, that ez far ez I can see
Beats euchre, poker, and van-toon, they calls the 'Spellin' Bee.' "

Then Brown of Calaveras simply hitched his chair and spake,
"Poker is good enough for me," and Lanky Jim sez, "Shake!"
And Bob allowed he warn't proud, but he "must say right thar
That the man who tackled euchre hed his education squar."
This brought up Lenny Fairchild, the schoolmaster, who said
He knew the game, and he would give instructions on that head.

"For instance, take some simple word," sez he, "like 'separate':
Now who can spell it?" Dog my skin, ef thar was one in eight.
This set the boys all wild at once. The chairs was put in row,
And at the head was Lanky Jim, and at the foot was Joe,
And high upon the bar itself the schoolmaster was raised,
And the barkeep put his glasses down, and sat and silent gazed.

The first word out was "parallel," and seven let it be,
Till Joe waltzed in his "double l" betwixt the "a" and "e";
For since he drilled them Mexicans in San Jacinto's fight
Thar warn't no prouder man got up than Pistol Joe that night—
Till "rhythm" came! He tried to smile, then said "they had him
    there,"
And Lanky Jim, with one long stride, got up and took his chair.

O little kids, my pretty kids, 'twas touchin' to survey
These bearded men, with weppings on, like schoolboys at their
    play.
They'd laugh with glee, and shout to see each other lead the van,
And Bob sat up as monitor with a cue for a rattan,
Till the Chair gave out "incinerate," and Brown said he'd be
    durned
If any such blamed word as that in school was ever learned.

When "phthisis" came they all sprang up, and vowed the man
    who rung
Another blamed Greek word on them be taken out and hung.
As they sát down again I saw in Bilson's eye a flash,
And Brown of Calaveras was a-twistin' his moustache,
And when at last Brown slipped on "gneiss," and Bilson took his
    chair,

He dropped some casual words about some folks who dyed their
   hair.

And then the Chair grew very white, and the Chair said he'd
   adjourn,
But Poker Dick remarked that *he* would wait and get his turn;
Then with a tremblin' voice and hand, and with a wanderin' eye,
The Chair next offered "eider-duck," and Dick began with "I,"
And Bilson smiled—then Bilson shrieked! Just how the fight begun
I never knowed, for Bilson dropped, and Dick, he moved up one.

Then certain gents arose and said "they'd business down in camp,"
And "ez the road was rather dark, and ez the night was damp,
They'd"—here got up Three-fingered Jack and locked the door and
   yelled:
"No, not one mother's son goes out till that thar word is spelled!"
But while the words were on his lips, he groaned and sank in pain,
And sank with Webster on his chest and Worcester on his brain.

Below the bar dodged Poker Dick, and tried to look ez he
Was huntin' up authorities thet no one else could see;
And Brown got down behind the stove, allowin' he "was cold,"
Till it upsot and down his legs the cinders freely rolled,
And several gents called "Order!" till in his simple way
Poor Smith began with "O-r"—"Or"—and he was dragged away.

O little kids, my pretty kids, down on your knees and pray!
You've got your eddication in a peaceful sort of way;
And bear in mind thar may be sharps ez slings their spellin'
   square,
But likewise slings their bowie knives without a thought or care.
You wants to know the rest, my dears? Thet's all! In me you see
The only gent that lived to tell about the Spellin' Bee!

He ceased and passed, that truthful man; the children went their
   way
With downcast heads and downcast hearts—but not to sport or
   play.

For when at eve the lamps were lit, and supperless to bed
Each child was sent, with tasks undone and lessons all unsaid,
No man might know the awful woe that thrilled their youthful
　　frames,
As they dreamed of Angels' Spelling Bee and thought of Truthful
　　James.

BRET HARTE

The Bushrangers

Four horsemen rode out from the heart of the range,
Four horsemen with aspects forbidding and strange.
They were booted and spurred, they were armed to the teeth,
And they frowned as they looked on the valley beneath,
As forward they rode through the rocks and the fern—
Ned Kelly, Dan Kelly, Steve Hart, and Joe Byrne.

Ned Kelly drew rein and he shaded his eyes—
"The town's at our mercy! See yonder it lies!
To hell with the troopers!"—he shook his clenched fist—
"We will shoot them like dogs if they dare to resist!"
And all of them nodded, grim-visaged and stern—
Ned Kelly, Dan Kelly, Steve Hart, and Joe Byrne.

Through the gullies and creeks they rode silently down;
They stuck-up the station and raided the town;
They opened the safe and they looted the bank;
They laughed and were merry, they ate and they drank.
Then off to the ranges they went with their gold—
Oh! never were bandits more reckless and bold.

But time brings its punishment, time travels fast—
And the outlaws were trapped in Glenrowan at last,
Where three of them died in the smoke and the flame,

And Ned Kelly came back—to the last he was game.
But the Law shot him down (he was fated to hang),
And that was the end of the bushranging gang.

Whatever their faults and whatever their crimes,
Their deeds lend romance to those faraway times.
They have gone from the gullies they haunted of old,
And nobody knows where they buried their gold.
To the ranges they loved they will never return—
Ned Kelly, Dan Kelly, Steve Hart, and Joe Byrne.

But at times when I pass through that sleepy old town
Where the far-distant peaks of Strathbogie look down
I think of the days when those grim ranges rang
To the galloping hooves of the bushranging gang.
Though the years bring oblivion, time brings a change,
The ghosts of the Kellys still ride from the range.

EDWARD HARRINGTON

At Sea

The Clipper Dunbar to the Clipper Cutty Sark

When you're sailing in strange harbors, *Cutty Sark, Cutty Sark,*
With the linesman calling soundings by the Mark,
    Do you hear my faint Ahoy?
    As you're picking up the buoy,
    Do you hear my faint Ahoy?
             Cutty Sark.

I once sailed as you do now, *Cutty Sark, Cutty Sark,*
Bending mast and dipping prow, *Cutty Sark,*
    I once knew the winds' wild way,
    And the salt Pacific spray,
    And the deep sea's sound and sway,
             Cutty Sark.

Oh, the black night long ago, *Cutty Sark, Cutty Sark,*
Far from home and Plymouth Hoe, *Cutty Sark,*
    When we drove for Sydney Head,
    And took the Gap instead,
    Oh, we took the Gap instead,
             Cutty Sark.

When you're sailing in strange harbors, *Cutty Sark, Cutty Sark,*
With the linesman calling soundings by the Mark,
    In fathoms deeper far
    Then deep sea fishes are,
    Salute the lost *Dunbar,*
             Cutty Sark.

ETHEL ANDERSON

Christmas at Sea

The sheets were frozen hard, and they cut the naked hand;
The decks were like a slide, where a seaman scarce could stand;
The wind was a nor'wester, blowing squally off the sea;
And cliffs and spouting breakers were the only things a-lee.

They heard the surf a-roaring before the break of day;
But 'twas only with the peep of light we saw how ill we lay.
We tumbled every hand on deck instanter, with a shout,
And we gave her the maintops'l, and stood by to go about.

All day we tacked and tacked between the South Head and the
    North;
All day we hauled the frozen sheets, and got no further forth;
All day as cold as charity, in bitter pain and dread,
For very life and nature we tacked from head to head.

We gave the South a wider berth, for there the tide race roared;
But every tack we made we brought the North Head close aboard:
So's we saw the cliffs and houses, and the breakers running high,
And the coastguard in his garden, with his glass against his eye.

The frost was on the village roofs as white as ocean foam;
The good red fires were burning bright in every longshore home;
The windows sparkled clear, and the chimneys volleyed out;
And I vow we sniffed the victuals as the vessel went about.

The bells upon the church were rung with a mighty jovial cheer;
For it's just that I should tell you how (of all days in the year)
This day of our adversity was blessèd Christmas morn,
And the house above the coastguard's was the house where I was
    born.

O well I saw the pleasant room, the pleasant faces there,
My mother's silver spectacles, my father's silver hair;

And well I saw the firelight, like a flight of homely elves,
Go dancing round the china plates that stand upon the shelves.

And well I knew the talk they had, the talk that was of me,
Of the shadow on the household and the son that went to sea;
And O the wicked fool I seemed, in every kind of way,
To be here and hauling frozen ropes on blessèd Christmas Day.

They lit the high sea-light, and the dark began to fall.
"All hands to loose topgallant sails," I heard the captain call.
"By the Lord, she'll never stand it," our first mate, Jackson, cried.
. . . "It's the one way or the other, Mr. Jackson," he replied.

She staggered to her bearings, but the sails were new and good,
And the ship smelt up to windward just as though she understood.
As the winter's day was ending, in the entry of the night,
We cleared the weary headland, and passed below the light.

And they heaved a mighty breath, every soul on board but me,
As they saw her nose again pointing handsome out to sea;
But all that I could think of, in the darkness and the cold,
Was just that I was leaving home and my folks were growing old.

ROBERT LOUIS STEVENSON

The Yarn of the Loch Achray

The *Loch Achray* was a clipper tall
With seven-and-twenty hands in all.
Twenty to hand and reef and haul,
A skipper to sail and mates to bawl
"Tally on to the tackle fall,
Heave now 'n' start her, heave 'n' pawl!"
Hear the yarn of a sailor,
An old yarn learned at sea.

Her crew were shipped and they said "Farewell,
So long, my Tottie, my lovely gel;
We sail today if we fetch to hell,
It's time we tackled the wheel a spell."
     Hear the yarn of a sailor,
     An old yarn learned at sea.

The dockside loafers talked on the quay
The day that she towed down to sea:
"Lord, what a handsome ship she be!
Cheer her, sonny boys, three times three!"
And the dockside loafers gave her a shout
As the red-funnelled tugboat towed her out;
They gave her a cheer as the custom is,
And the crew yelled, "Take our loves to Liz—
Three cheers, bullies, for old Pier Head
'N' the bloody stay-at-homes!" they said.
     Hear the yarn of a sailor,
     An old yarn learned at sea.

In the gray of the coming on of night
She dropped the tug at the Tuskar Light,
'N' the topsails went to the topmast head
To a chorus that fairly awoke the dead.
She trimmed her yards and slanted south
With her royals set and a bone in her mouth.
     Hear the yarn of a sailor,
     An old yarn learned at sea.

She crossed the Line and all went well,
They ate, they slept, and they struck the bell,
And I give you a gospel truth when I state
The crowd didn't find any fault with the Mate,
But one night off of the River Plate.
     Hear the yarn of a sailor,
     An old yarn learned at sea.

It freshened up till it blew like thunder
And burrowed her deep lee scuppers under.
The old man said, "I mean to hang on
Till her canvas busts or her sticks are gone"—
Which the blushing looney did, till at last
Overboard went her mizzenmast.
    Hear the yarn of a sailor,
    An old yarn learned at sea.

Then a fierce squall struck the *Loch Achray*
And bowed her down to her waterway;
Her main shrouds gave and her forestay,
And a green sea carried her wheel away;
Ere the watch below had time to dress
She was cluttered up in a blushing mess.
    Hear the yarn of a sailor,
    An old yarn learned at sea.

She couldn't lay to nor yet pay off,
And she got swept clean in the bloody trough;
Her masts were gone, and afore you knowed
She filled by the head and down she goed.
Her crew make seven-and-twenty dishes
For the big jack sharks and the little fishes,
And over their bones the water swishes.
    Hear the yarn of a sailor,
    An old yarn learned at sea.

The wives and girls they watch in the rain
For a ship as won't come home again.
"I reckon it's them head winds," they say,
"She'll be home tomorrow, if not today.
I'll just nip home 'n' I'll air the sheets
'N' buy the fixins 'n' cook the meats
As my man likes 'n' as my man eats."

So home they goes by the windy streets,
Thinking their men are homeward bound
With anchors hungry for English ground,
And the bloody fun of it is, they're drowned!
    Hear the yarn of a sailor,
    An old yarn learned at sea.

JOHN MASEFIELD

The Old Navy

The captain stood on the carronade: "First Lieutenant," says he,
"Send all my merry men aft here, for they must list to me;
I haven't the gift of the gab, my sons—because I'm bred to the sea;
That ship there is a Frenchman, who means to fight with we.
  And odds bobs, hammer and tongs, long as I've been to sea,
  I've fought 'gainst every odds—but I've gained the victory!

"That ship there is a Frenchman, and if we don't take she,
'Tis a thousand bullets to one, that she will capture we;
I haven't the gift of the gab, my boys; so each man to his gun;
If she's not mine in half an hour, I'll flog each mother's son.
  For odds bobs, hammer and tongs, long as I've been to sea,
  I've fought 'gainst every odds—and I've gained the victory!"

We fought for twenty minutes, when the Frenchman had enough;
"I little thought," said he, "that your men were of such stuff."
Our captain took the Frenchman's sword, a low bow made to he;
"I haven't the gift of the gab, monsieur, but polite I wish to be.
  And odds bobs, hammer and tongs, long as I've been to sea,
  I've fought 'gainst every odds—but I've gained the victory!"

Our captain sent for all of us: "My merry men," said he,
"I haven't the gift of the gab, my lads, but yet I thankful be;
You've done your duty handsomely, each man stood to his gun;

If you hadn't, you villains, as sure as day, I'd have flogged each
    mother's son,
  For odds bobs, hammer and tongs, as long as I've been to sea,
  I'll fight 'gainst every odds—and I'll gain the victory!"

FREDERICK MARRYAT

The Caulker

A FISH STORY

("A whaler whose plates had been pierced was saved by a
large fish which was drawn into the hole by the inrush of
water and got jammed there. The fish only became dislodged
when they were nearly in port."—*Daily Paper.*)

A strong imagination from my youth has been combined
With insatiate love of detail and a quick inquiring mind;
I have therefore made an effort at discovering what are
The actual facts that lie behind this interesting par.

It was the whaler *Whatshername*—I'm not allowed to state
The tonnage, destination, nationality, or date—
But anyway a rock (or wreck) nigh brought her to her doom
And made a most impressive hole abaft the engine room.

The hole was very large indeed; at once the water rolled
Unhindered through the orifice and swamped the afterhold;
And very soon, unless the crew could reach a port and dock her,
The whole concern would go for good to Davy Jones's locker.

All hands were piped to man the pumps, and manfully they
    pumped,
While feverishly up and down the bridge the skipper stumped;
But stumped the "Old Man" ne'er so fast nor pumped the men so
    hard,
The water in the afterhold was gaining yard by yard.

"We're lost!" the captain cried. "That's so," the mate he made
    reply.
"Then man the boats," the skipper said, a tear in either eye;
But scarcely had he wiped them off and dried them on his trouser
When a sailor ran and cried, "The pumps are gaining now, sir."

Yes, fate had acted in a way as kind as it was odd;
In point of actual fact, some fish—a conger or a cod,
A whale or shark (though which it was I really mustn't say)—
Drawn by the inrush through the hole, had stuck and blocked the
    way.

This for the moment saved the crew from quite a pretty pickle,
For now the flood that raged before became the merest trickle.
"Then pump again!" the captain cried. The mate remarked, "Ay,
    ay!"
And very soon the afterhold was practically dry.

"Full steam ahead!" the skipper said. "Make for the nearest land!"
"Ay, ay, sir," said the mate—when up there rushed a fo'c's'le
    hand.
"Excusing me the liberty o' speakin', sir," he said,
"They've pumped the blinkin' 'old so dry the bung'll soon be
    dead."

"Why not, my man?" the captain cried. The mate re-echoed,
    "Why?"
The man replied, "It don't seem fair ter let the creetur die;
But quite apart from gratitood I've 'eard it said, I think,
That fish wot die will quickly dry, and then o' course they shrink."

"The deuce they do!" the captain cried. The mate said, "Gad, he's
    right!
The sea will push him in unless we keep her watertight."
"Go, fill the biggest pail we've got," the ingenious skipper said,
"With water to the brim and hold it round the fish's head."

Then straight that seaman hurries to the water cask and fills
The largest pail with water and he holds it round his gills;
But even then, although the stuff did cheer him up a bit,
It still was clear that kindly fish felt very far from fit.

The captain watched with twitching lips; the mate began to curse;
The fish was shrinking rapidly, it fitted worse and worse;
The water poured in tons aboard; the fish still shrank and shrank,
Until at last it slipped right in, and then the good ship sank.

The shore was near; the crew were saved and reached their native
    land;
But still the skipper and the mate can never understand
Exactly why a fish should die with water round its head.
"We can't have *drowned* it?" asked the mate. "Why, no," the
    skipper said.

But in the crew was one who knew and sadly slunk away—
His conscience needs must trouble him until his dying day—
The fo'c's'le hand. "My fault!" he groans. "It's all my silly fault;
I gave the brute *fresh* water, when of course he wanted *salt*."

M. A. LEWIS

Cape Horn Gospel—1

"I was in a hooker once," said Karlssen,
"And Bill, as was a seaman, died,
So we lashed him in an old tarpaulin
And tumbled him across the side;
And the fun of it was that all his gear was
Divided up among the crew
Before that blushing human error,
Our crawling little captain, knew.

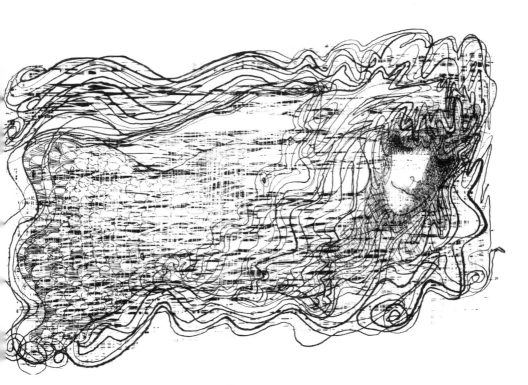

"On the passage home one morning
(As certain as I prays for grace)
There was old Bill's shadder a-hauling
At the weather mizzen-topsail brace.
He was all grown green with seaweed,
He was all lashed up and shored;
So I says to him, I says, 'Why, Billy!
What's a-bringin' of you back aboard?'

" 'I'm a-weary of them there mermaids,'
Says old Bill's ghost to me;
'It ain't no place for a Christian
Below there—under sea.
For it's all blown sand and shipwrecks,
And old bones eaten bare,
And them cold fishy females
With long green weeds for hair.' "

JOHN MASEFIELD

A Nautical Extravaganza

I stood one day by the breezy bay
    A-watching the ships go by,
When a tired tar said, with a shake of his head:
    "I wisht I could tell a lie!

"I've seen some sights as would jigger yer lights
    And they've jiggered me own, in sooth,
But I ain't wuth a darn at spinnin' a yarn
    What wanders away from the truth.

"We were out in the gig, the Rigagajig,
    Jest a mile and a half to sea,
When Capting Snook, with a troubled look,
    He came and he says to me:

" 'O Bos'n Smith, make haste forthwith
    And hemstitch the fo'ard sail;
Accordion pleat the dory sheet,
    For there's going to be a gale!'

"I straightway did as the capting bid—
    No sooner the job was through
When the north wind, whoof, bounced over the roof
    And, murderin' lights, she blew!

"She blew the tars right off the spars,
    And the spars right off the mast,
Sails and pails and anchors and nails
    Flew by on the wings o' the blast.

"The galley shook as she blew our cook
    Straight out o' the porthole glim,
While pots and pans, kettles and cans
    Went clatterin' after him.

"She blew the fire from our gallant stove
    And the coal from our gallant bin,
She whistled apace past the capting's face
    And blew the beard off his chin!

" 'O wizzel me dead!' the capting said
    (And the words blew out of his mouth);
'We're lost, I fear, if the wind don't veer
    And blow a while from the south.'

"And wizzel me dead, no sooner he'd said
    Them words that blew from his mouth,
Then the wind switched round with a hurricane sound
    And blew straight in from the south.

"We opened our eyes with a wild surprise,
    And never a word to say—
In changin' her tack the wind blew back
    The things that she'd blew away!

"She blew the tars back onto the spars,
    And the spars back onto the mast;
Back flew the pails, the sails and the nails,
    Which into the ship stuck fast.

"And 'fore we could look she blew back the cook
    Straight into the galley coop,
Back dropped the pans, the kettles and cans,
    Without even spillin' the soup.

"She blew the fire back into the stove
    Where it burnt in its proper place—
And all of us cheered as she blew the beard
    Back on the capting's face.

"There's more o' me tale," said the sailor hale,
    "As would jigger yer lights, in sooth,

But I ain't wuth a darn at spinnin' a yarn
What wanders away from the truth."

WALLACE IRWIN

The Figurehead

A SALT SEA YARN

There was an ancient carver that carved of a saint,
But the parson wouldn't have it, so he took a pot of paint
And changed its angel garment for a dashing soldier rig,
And said it was a figurehead and sold it to a brig.

The brig hauled her mainsail to an offshore draught,
Then she shook her snowy royals and the Scillies went abaft;
And cloudy with her canvas she ran before the Trade
Till she got to the Equator, where she struck a merrymaid.

A string of pearls and conches were all of her togs,
But the flying fish and porpoises they followed her like dogs;
She had a voice of silver and lips of coral red,
She climbed the dolphin-striker and kissed the figurehead.

Then every starry evening she'd swim in the foam
About the bows, a-singing like a nightingale at Home;
She'd call to him and sing to him as sweetly as a bird;
But the wooden-headed effigy he never said a word.

And every starry evening in the doldrum calms
She'd wriggle up the bobstay and throw her tender arms
About his scarlet shoulders and fondle him and cry
And stroke his curly whiskers, but he never winked an eye.

She couldn't get an answer to her tears or moans,
So she went and told her daddy, told the ancient Davy Jones;
Old Davy damned his eyesight and puzzled of his wits,
Then whistled up his hurricanes and tore the brig to bits.

Down on the ocean bed, green fathoms deep,
Where the wrecks lie rotting and great sea serpents creep
In a gleaming grotto all built of sailors' bones,
Sits the handsome figurehead, listening to Miss Jones.

Songs o' love she sings him the livelong day,
And she hangs upon his bosom and sobs the night away,
But he never, never answers, for beneath his soldier paint
The wooden-headed lunatic still thinks that he's a saint.

CROSBIE GARSTIN

Sea Change

"Goneys an' gullies an' all o' the birds o' the sea,
They ain't no birds, not really," said Billy the Dane.
"Not mollies, nor gullies, nor goneys at all," said he,
"But simply the sperrits of mariners livin' again.

"Them birds goin' fishin' is nothin' but souls o' the drowned,
Souls o' the drowned an' the kicked as are never no more;
An' that there haughty old albatross cruisin' around,
Belike he's Admiral Nelson or Admiral Noah.

"An' merry's the life they are living. They settle and dip,
They fishes, they never stands watches, they waggle their wings;
When a ship comes by, they fly to look at the ship
To see how the nowaday mariners manages things.

"When freezing aloft in a snorter, I tell you I wish—
(Though maybe it ain't like a Christian)—I wish I could be
A haughty old copper-bound albatross dipping for fish
And coming the proud over all o' the birds o' the sea."

JOHN MASEFIELD

The Powerful Eyes o' Jeremy Tait

An old sea dog on a sailor's log
    Thus spake to a passerby:
"The most onnatteral thing on earth
    Is the power o' the human eye—
Oh, bless me! yes, oh, blow me! yes—
    It's the power o' the human eye!

"We'd left New York en route for Cork
    A day and a half to sea,
When Jeremy Tait, our fourteenth mate,
    He fastened his eyes on me.

"And wizzle me hook! 'twas a powerful look
    That flashed from them eyes o' his;
I was terrified from heart to hide
    And chilled to me bones and friz.

" 'O Jeremy Tait, O fourteenth mate,'
    I hollers with looks askance,
'Full well I wist ye're a hypnotist,
    So please to remove yer glance!'

"But Jeremy laughed as he turned abaft
    His glance like a demon rat,
And he frightened the cook with his piercin' look,
    And he startled the captain's cat.

"Oh me, oh my! When he turned his eye
  On our very efficient crew,
They fell like dead, or they stood like lead
  And stiff as a poker grew.

"So early and late did Jeremy Tait
  That talent o' his employ,
Which caused the crew, and the captain, too,
  Some moments of great annoy.

"For we loved J. Tait, our fourteenth mate
  As an officer brave and true,
But we quite despised bein' hypnotized
  When we had so much work to do.

"So we grabbed J. Tait, our fourteenth mate
  (His eyes bein' turned away),
By collar and sleeve, and we gave a heave,
  And chucked him into the spray.

"His eyes they flashed as in he splashed,
  But this glance it was sent too late,
For close to our bark a man-eatin' shark
  Jumped after Jeremy Tait.

"And you can bet he would ha' been et
  If he hadn't have did as he done—
Straight at the shark an optical spark
  From his terrible eye he spun.

"Then the shark he shook at Jeremy's look
  And he quailed at Jeremy's glance;
Then he gave a sort of a sharkery snort
  And fell right into a trance!

"Quite mesmerized and hypnotized
  That submarine monster lay;

Meek as a shrimp, with his fins all limp,
   He silently floated away.

"So we all of us cried with a conscious pride,
   'Hurrah for Jeremy Tait!'
And we hove a line down into the brine
   And reskied him from his fate.

"And the captain cries, 'We kin use them eyes
   To mighty good purpose soon.
Men, spread the sails—we're a-goin' for whales,
   And we don't need nary harpoon.

" 'For when we hail a blubberous whale
   A-spoutin' the water high,
We'll sail up bold and knock 'im cold
   With the power o' Jeremy's eye!' "

And thus on his log the old sea dog
   Sat whittling nautical chips:
"Oh, powerf'ler far than the human eye
   Is the truth o' the human lips;
But rarest of all is the pearls that fall
   From a truthful mariner's lips."

WALLACE IRWIN

Lord Arnaldos

¿QUIEN HUBIESE TAL VENTURA?

The strangest of adventures,
That happen by the sea,
Befell to Lord Arnaldos
On the Evening of St. John;
  For he was out a-hunting—

A huntsman bold was he!—
When he beheld a little ship
And close to land was she.
Her cords were all of silver,
Her sails of cramasy;
And he who sailed the little ship
Was singing at the helm:
The waves stood still to hear him,
The wind was soft and low;
The fish who dwell in darkness
Ascended through the sea,
And all the birds in heaven
Flew down to his mast tree.
Then spake the Lord Arnaldos,
(Well shall you hear his words!)
"Tell me for God's sake, sailor,
What song may that song be?"
The sailor spake in answer,
And answer thus made he:
"I only tell my song to those
Who sail away with me."

JAMES ELROY FLECKER

The Story of Samuel Jackson

I'll tell you of a sailor now, a tale that can't be beat,
His name was Samuel Jackson, and his height was seven feet;
And how this man was shipwrecked in the far Pacific Isles,
And of the heathen natives with their suppositious wiles.

Now when the others cut the ship, because she was a wreck,
They left this Samuel Jackson there, a-standin' on the deck—
That is, a standin' on the deck, while sittin' on the boom;
They wouldn't let him in the boat 'cos he took up too much room.

When up there came a tilted wave, and like a horse it romped,
It fell like mountains on the boat, and so the boat was swamped;
And of those selfish mariners full every one was drowned,
While Samuel, standing on the deck, beheld it safe and sound.

Now when the sea grew soft and still, and all the gale was o'er,
Sam Jackson made himself a raft, and paddled safe ashore.
For fear of fatal accidents—not knowin' what might come—
He took a gun and matches, with a prudent cask of rum.

Now this island where he landed proved as merry as a fife,
For its indigents had ne'er beheld a white man in their life;
Such incidents as rum and guns they never yet had seen,
And likewise, in religion, they were awful jolly green.

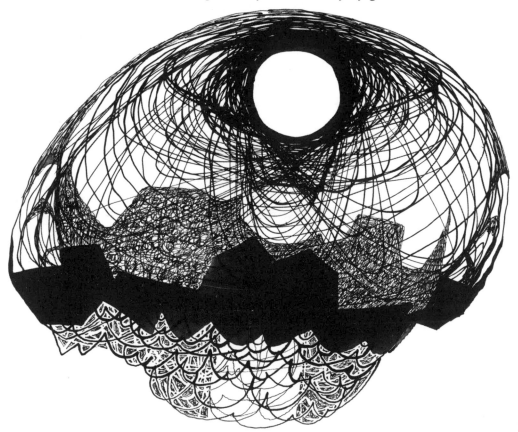

But they had a dim tradition, from their ancestors, in course,
Which they had somehow *de*rived from a very ancient source:
How that a god would come to them, and set the island right;
And how he should be orful tall, and likewise pearly white.

Now when they saw this Samuel approachin' on his raft,
The news through all the island shades was quickly telegraft,
How all their tribulat-i-ons would speedily be past,
'Cos the long-expected sucker was invadin' 'em at last.

Now when Sam Jackson stept ashore, as modest as you please,
Nine thousand bloomin' savages received him on their knees;
He looked around in wonderment, regardin' it as odd,
Not bein' much accustomed to be worshipped as a god.

But he twigged the situation, and with a pleasin' smile
Stretched out his hands, a-blessin' all the natives of the isle;
He did it well, although his paws were bigger than a pan,
Because he was habitual a most politeful man.

So to return their manners, and nary-wise for fun,
He raised himself with dignity, and then fired off his gun:
So all allowed that he must be one of the heavenly chaps,
Since he went about with lightning and dispensed with thunder-
    claps.

They took him on their shoulders, and he let it go for good,
And went into their city in the which a temple stood,
And sot him on the altar, and made him their salams,
And brought him pleasant coco-nuts, with chickens, po, and yams.

And from that day henceforward, in a captivating style,
He relegated, as he pleased, the natives of that isle;
And when an unbeliever rose—as now and then were some,
He cured their irreligion with a little taste of rum.

He settled all their business, and he did it very well,
So everything went booming like a blessed wedding bell;
Eleven lovely feminines attended to his wants,
And a guard of honor followed him to all his usual haunts.

Now what mortal men are made of, that they can't put up with
     bliss,
I do not know, but this I know, that Sam got tired of this;
He wished that he was far away, again aboard a ship,
And all he thought of—night and day—was givin' 'em the slip.

And so one night when all was still and every soul asleep,
He got into a good canoe and paddled o'er the deep,
But oh the row the natives made, when early in the morn
They came to worship Samuel, and found their god was gone!

Then Samuel traveled many days, but had the luck at last
To meet a brig from Boston where he shipped before the mast;
And he gave it as his sentiments, and no one thought it odd,
He was better off as sailor than when sailing as a god.

Now many years had flown away when Samuel was forgot,
There came a ship for pearl shell unto that lonely spot;
They went into the temple, and what do you suppose
They found the natives worshipping—a suit of Samuel's clothes!

And this was the tradition of the people of the soil,
How once a great divinity had ruled upon their isle;
Four fathoms tall, with eyes like fire, and such was their believin',
One night he got upon the moon—and sailed away to Heaven!

CHARLES GODFREY LELAND

The Eddystone Light

Me father was the keeper of the Eddystone Light,
He married a mer-my-aid one night;
Out of the match came children three—
Two was fish and the other was me.

> CHORUS: Jolly stories, jolly told
> When the winds is bleak and the nights is cold;
> No such life can be led on the shore
> As is had on the rocks by the ocean's roar.

When I was but a boyish chip,
They put me in charge of the old lightship;
I trimmed the lamps and I filled 'em with oil,
And I played seven-up accordin' to Hoyle.

> CHORUS: Jolly stories, jolly told
> When the winds is bleak and the nights is cold;
> No such life can be led on the shore
> As is had on the rocks by the ocean's roar.

One evenin' as I was a-trimmin' the glim
An' singin' a verse of the evenin' hymn,
I see by the light of me binnacle lamp
Me kind old father lookin' jolly and damp;
An' a voice from the starboard shouted "Ahoy!"
An' there was me gran'mother sittin' on a buoy—
Meanin' a buoy for ships what sail
An' not a boy what's a juvenile male.

> CHORUS: Jolly stories, jolly told
> When the winds is bleak and the nights is cold;
> No such life can be led on the shore
> As is had on the rocks by the ocean's roar.

ENGLISH FOLK SONG

Hell's Pavement

"When I'm discharged in Liverpool 'n' draws my bit o' pay,
  I won't come to sea no more.
I'll court a pretty little lass 'n' have a weddin' day,
  'N' settle somewhere down ashore.

"I'll never fare to sea again a-temptin' Davy Jones,
A-hearkening to the cruel sharks a-hungerin' for my bones;
I'll run a blushin' dairy farm or go a-crackin' stones,
  Or buy 'n' keep a little liquor store"—
                              So he said.

They towed her in to Liverpool, we made the hooker fast,
  And the copper-bound officials paid the crew,
And Billy drew his money, but the money didn't last,
  For he painted the alongshore blue—

It was rum for Poll, and rum for Nan, and gin for Jolly Jack.
He shipped a week later in the clothes upon his back,
He had to pinch a little straw, he had to beg a sack
  To sleep on, when his watch was through—
                              So he did.

JOHN MASEFIELD

The Ballad of Hagensack

I'd been away a year, a year
  A-sailing of the main
When I came back to Hagensack
  To see the town again.

"I oughter weep," says I, says I—
 "I wonder why I don't?
I know I shan't—perhaps I can't,
 Perhaps again I won't.

"But where is all the friends, the friends
 What once was blithe and free?
I look to find that they have pined
 Away with thoughts o' me."

And so I sought the house, the house
 Where lived me old friend, Bill.
" 'Tis sad," I said, "to think he's dead—
 To think that grief can kill!"

"Is big Bill Smith to home, to home,
 Is Smith to home?" says I.
"Oh yes, he's here a-drinkin' beer
 And larkin' to the sky."

"A-larkin' to the sky!" says I,
 "And him, the faithless bloke,
Was that bereft the day I left
 I thought that he would croke."

Then I thought of Mamie Jones,-mie Jones,
 What was me finansay;
It seemed that she, in decency,
 Would have to pine away.

"Is Mamie Jones to home, to home,
 Her that was deep enthralled?"
"Oh, no, she's out with Mister Prout—
 I'll tell her that you called."

"Oh that you needn't do,-dn't do,
 You needn't do that same.

Why ain't she cold beneath the mold?—
  O careless, careless Mame!

"One time I read about, about
  A tar named Tim McGee
And people sighed and up and died
  The day he put to sea;

"But not in Hagensack,-ensack
  Was such a story writ,
For I believe the more I leave
  The healthier they git."

Then straight I went and put, and put
  A turnip on a stick
And with a tack wrote, "HAGENSACK,
  THE FICKLEST OF THE FICK."

And then I took the turnip up
  And fed it to a cow.
"I'll ne'er go back to Hagensack,"
  I says, and kept me vow.

                        WALLACE IRWIN

Odd
and Funny

The Smoked Herring

There was a great white wall—bare, bare, bare,
Against the wall a ladder—high, high, high,
And, on the ground, a smoked herring—dry, dry, dry.

He comes bearing in his hands—so dirty, dirty, dirty,
A heavy hammer, a great nail—sharp, sharp, sharp,
A ball of string—so big, big, big.

Then he climbs the ladder—high, high, high,
And drives the pointed nail—toc, toc, toc,
Into the top of the great white wall—bare, bare, bare.

He lets the hammer go—it falls, falls, falls,
Ties to the nail the string—so long, long, long,
And, to the end, the smoked herring—dry, dry, dry.

He descends the ladder—so high, high, high,
Carries it away, with the hammer—so heavy, heavy, heavy,
And so he goes away—far, far, far.

And ever since the smoked herring—dry, dry, dry,
At the end of the string—so long, long, long,
Very slowly swings—for ever, ever, ever.

I have made up this little tale—so simple, simple, simple,
Just to enrage people—so grave, grave, grave,
And to amuse children—so small, small, small.

CHARLES CROS
(Translated from the French by A. L. LLOYD)

My First Cigar

'Twas just behind the woodshed,
    One glorious summer day,
Far o'er the hills the sinking sun
    Pursued his westward way;
And in my safe seclusion
    Removed from all the jar
And din of earth's confusion
    I smoked my first cigar.

    It was my first cigar!
    It was the worst cigar!
Raw, green and dank, hidebound and rank,
    It was my first cigar!

Ah, bright the boyish fancies
    Wrapped in the smoke-wreaths blue;
My eyes grew dim, my head was light,
    The woodshed round me flew!
Dark night closed in around me—
    Black night, without a star—
Grim death methought had found me
    And spoiled my first cigar.

    It was my first cigar!
    A six-for-five cigar!
No viler torch the air could scorch—
    It was my first cigar!

All pallid was my beaded brow,
    The reeling night was late,
My startled mother cried in fear,
    "My child, what have you ate?"

I heard my father's smothered laugh,
    It seemed so strange and far,
I knew he knew I knew he knew
    I'd smoked my first cigar!

    It was my first cigar!
    A give-away cigar!
I could not die—I knew not why—
    It was my first cigar!

Since then I've stood in reckless ways,
    I've dared what men can dare,
I've mocked at danger, walked with death,
    I've laughed at pain and care.
I do not dread what may befall
    'Neath my malignant star,
No frowning fate again can make
    Me smoke my first cigar.

    I've smoked my first cigar!
    My first and worst cigar!
Fate has no terrors for the man
    Who's smoked his first cigar!

ROBERT J. BURDETTE

The Embarrassing Episode of Little Miss Muffet

Little Miss Muffet discovered a tuffet,
    (Which never occurred to the rest of us)
And, as 'twas a June day, and just about noonday,
    She wanted to eat—like the best of us:
Her diet was whey, and I hasten to say

It is wholesome and people grow fat on it.
The spot being lonely, the lady not only
   Discovered the tuffet, but sat on it.

A rivulet gabbled beside her and babbled,
   As rivulets always are thought to do,
And dragon flies sported around and cavorted,
   As poets say dragon flies ought to do;
When, glancing aside for a moment, she spied
   A horrible sight that brought fear to her,
A hideous spider was sitting beside her,
   And most unavoidably near to her!

Albeit unsightly, this creature politely
   Said: "Madam, I earnestly vow to you,
I'm penitent that I did not bring my hat. I
   Should otherwise certainly bow to you."
Though anxious to please, he was so ill at ease
   That he lost all his sense of propriety,
And grew so inept that he clumsily stept
   In her plate—which is barred in Society.

This curious error completed her terror;
   She shuddered, and growing much paler, not
Only left her tuffet, but dealt him a buffet
   Which doubled him up in a sailor knot.
It should be explained that at this he was pained;
   He cried: "I have vexed you, no doubt of it!
Your fist's like a truncheon." "You're still in my luncheon,"
   Was all that she answered. "Get out of it!"

And the *Moral* is this: Be it madam or miss
   To whom you have something to say,
You are only absurd when you get in the curd,
   But you're rude when you get in the whey!

GUY WETMORE CARRYL

There Was an Old Woman

There was an old woman, as I've heard tell,
She went to the market, her eggs for to sell;
She went to market all on a market day.
And she fell asleep on the king's highway.

There came by a pedlar whose name was Stout;
He cut her petticoats all round about;
He cut her petticoats up to the knees,
Which made the old woman to shiver and freeze.

When this little woman did first wake,
She began to shiver and she began to shake;
She began to wonder and she began to cry,
"Oh! deary, deary me, this is none of I!

"But if it be I, as I do hope it be,
I've a little dog at home, and he'll know me;
If it be I, he'll wag his little tail,
And if it be not I, he'll loudly bark and wail."

Home went the little woman all in the dark;
Up got the little dog and he began to bark;
He began to bark, so she began to cry,
"Oh! deary, deary me, this is none of I!"

ANONYMOUS

The Doctor's Story

Good folks ever will have their way—
Good folks ever for it must pay.

But we, who are here and everywhere,
The burden of their faults must bear.

We must shoulder others' shame,
Fight their follies, and take their blame:

Purge the body, and humor the mind;
Doctor the eyes when the soul is blind;

Build the column of health erect
On the quicksands of neglect:

Always shouldering others' shame—
Bearing their faults and taking the blame!

Deacon Rogers, he came to me;
"Wife is a-goin' to die," said he.

"Doctors great, an' doctors small,
Haven't improved her any at all.

"Physic and blister, powders and pills,
And nothing sure but the doctors' bills!

"Twenty women, with remedies new,
Bother my wife the whole day through.

"Sweet as honey, or bitter as gall—
Poor old woman, she takes 'em all.

"Sour or sweet, whatever they choose;
Poor old woman, she daren't refuse.

"So she pleases whoe'er may call,
An' Death is suited the best of all.

"Physic and blister, powder an' pill—
Bound to conquer, and sure to kill!"

Mrs. Rogers lay in her bed,
Bandaged and blistered from foot to head.

Blistered and bandaged from head to toe,
Mrs. Rogers was very low.

Bottle and saucer, spoon and cup,
On the table stood bravely up;

Physics of high and low degree;
Calomel, catnip, boneset tea;

Everything a body could bear,
Excepting light and water and air.

I opened the blinds; the day was bright,
And God gave Mrs. Rogers some light.

I opened the window; the day was fair,
And God gave Mrs. Rogers some air.

Bottles and blisters, powders and pills,
Catnip, boneset, sirups and squills;

Drugs and medicines, high and low,
I threw them as far as I could throw.

"What are you doing?" my patient cried;
"Frightening Death," I coolly replied.

"You are crazy!" a visitor said:
I flung a bottle at his head.

Deacon Rogers he came to me;
"Wife is a-gettin' her health," said he.

"I really think she will worry through;
She scolds me just as she used to do.

"All the people have poohed an' slurred,
All the neighbors have had their word;

" 'Twere better to perish, some of 'em say,
Than be cured in such an irregular way."

"Your wife," said I, "had God's good care,
And His remedies, light and water and air.

"All of the doctors, beyond a doubt,
Couldn't have cured Mrs. Rogers without."

The deacon smiled and bowed his head;
"Then your bill is nothing," he said.

"God's be the glory, as you say!
God bless you, Doctor! Good day! Good day!"

If ever I doctor that woman again,
I'll give her medicine made by men.

WILL M. CARLETON

Autumn

Dick and Will and Charles and I
Were playing it was election day,
And I was running for president,
And Dick was a band that was going to play,

And Charles and Will were a street parade,
But Clarence came and said that he
Was going to run for president,
And I could run for school trustee.

He made some flags for Charles and Will
And a badge to go on Dickie's coat.
He stood some cornstalks by the fence
And had them for the men that vote.

Then he climbed on a box and made a speech
To the cornstalk men that were in a row.
It was all about the dem-o-crats,
And "I de-fy any man to show."

And "I de-fy any man to say."
And all about "It's a big disgrace."
He spoke his speech out very loud
And shook his fist in a cornstalk's face.

ELIZABETH MADOX ROBERTS

The Puzzled Census Taker

"Got any boys?" the Marshal said
    To a lady from over the Rhine;
And the lady shook her flaxen head,
    And civilly answered, *"Nein!"*

"Got any girls?" the Marshal said
    To the lady from over the Rhine;
And again the lady shook her head,
    And civilly answered, *"Nein!"*

"But some are dead?" the Marshal said
    To the lady from over the Rhine;
And again the lady shook her head,
    And civilly answered, *"Nein!"*

"Husband of course?" the Marshal said
    To the lady from over the Rhine;
And again she shook her flaxen head,
    And civilly answered, *"Nein!"*

"The devil you have!" the Marshal said
  To the lady from over the Rhine;
And again she shook her flaxen head,
  And civilly answered, *"Nein!"*

"Now what do you mean by shaking your head,
  And always answering 'Nine'?"
"Ich kann nicht Englisch!" civilly said
  The lady from over the Rhine!

JOHN GODFREY SAXE

Brown's Descent

OR, THE WILLY-NILLY SLIDE

Brown lived at such a lofty farm
  That everyone for miles could see
His lantern when he did his chores
  In winter after half-past three.

And many must have seen him make
  His wild descent from there one night,
'Cross lots, 'cross walls, 'cross everything,
  Describing rings of lantern light.

Between the house and barn the gale
  Got him by something he had on
And blew him out on the icy crust
  That cased the world, and he was gone!

Walls were all buried, trees were few:
  He saw no stay unless he stove
A hole in somewhere with his heel.
  But though repeatedly he strove

And stamped and said things to himself,
     And sometimes something seemed to yield,
He gained no foothold, but pursued
     His journey down from field to field.

Sometimes he came with arms outspread
     Like wings, revolving in the scene
Upon his longer axis, and
     With no small dignity of mien.

Faster or slower as he chanced,
     Sitting or standing as he chose,
According as he feared to risk
     His neck, or thought to spare his clothes.

He never let the lantern drop.
     And some exclaimed who saw afar
The figures he described with it,
     "I wonder what those signals are

Brown makes at such an hour of night!
     He's celebrating something strange.
I wonder if he's sold his farm,
     Or been made Master of the Grange."

He reeled, he lurched, he bobbed, he checked;
     He fell and made the lantern rattle
(But saved the light from going out.)
     So halfway down he fought the battle,

Incredulous of his own bad luck.
     And then becoming reconciled
To everything, he gave it up
     And came down like a coasting child.

"Well—I—be—" that was all he said,
     As standing in the river road,

He looked back up the slippery slope
  (Two miles it was) to his abode.

Sometimes as an authority
  On motorcars, I'm asked if I
Should say our stock was petered out,
  And this is my sincere reply:

Yankees are what they always were.
  Don't think Brown ever gave up hope
Of getting home again because
  He couldn't climb that slippery slope;

Or even thought of standing there
  Until the January thaw
Should take the polish off the crust.
  He bowed with grace to natural law,

And then went round it on his feet,
  After the manner of our stock;
Not much concerned for those to whom,
  At that particular time o'clock,

It must have looked as if the course
  He steered was really straight away
From that which he was headed for—
  Not much concerned for them, I say;

No more so than became a man—
  And politician at odd seasons.
I've kept Brown standing in the cold
  While I invested him with reasons;

But now he snapped his eyes three times;
  Then shook his lantern, saying, "Ile's
'Bout out!" and took the long way home
  By road, a matter of several miles.

ROBERT FROST

The Traveling Post Office

The roving breezes come and go, the reed beds sweep and sway,
The sleepy river murmurs low and loiters on its way,
It is the land of lots o' time along the Castlereagh. . . .

The old man's son had left the farm, he found it dull and slow,
He drifted to the great Northwest, where all the rovers go.
"He's gone so long," the old man said, "he's dropped right out of
    mind,
But if you'd write a line to him I'd take it very kind;
He's shearing here and fencing there, a kind of waif and stray—
He's droving now with Conroy's sheep along the Castlereagh.

"The sheep are traveling for the grass, and traveling very slow;
They may be at Mundooran now, or past the Overflow,
Or tramping down the blacksoil flats across by Waddiwong;
But all those little country towns would send the letter wrong—
The mailman, if he's extra tired, would pass them in his sleep.
It's safest to address the note to 'Care of Conroy's sheep,'
For five and twenty thousand head can scarcely go astray;
You write to 'Care of Conroy's sheep along the Castlereagh.' "

By rock and ridge and riverside the western mail has gone
Across the great Blue Mountain Range to take that letter on.
A moment on the topmost grade, while open fire-doors glare,
She pauses like a living thing to breathe the mountain air,
Then launches down the other side across the plains away
To bear that note to "Conroy's sheep along the Castlereagh."

And now by coach and mailman's bag it goes from town to town,
And Conroy's Gap and Conroy's Creek have marked it "Further
    down."
Beneath a sky of deepest blue, where never cloud abides,
A speck upon the waste of plain the lonely mailman rides.
Where fierce hot winds have set the pine and myall boughs asweep
He hails the shearers passing by for news of Conroy's sheep.

By big lagoons where wildfowl play and crested pigeons flock,
By campfires where the drovers ride around their restless stock,
And past the teamster toiling down to fetch the wool away
My letter chases Conroy's sheep along the Castlereagh.

A. B. ("BANJO") PATTERSON

The Boy Who Laughed at Santa Claus

In Baltimore there lived a boy.
He wasn't anybody's joy.
Although his name was Jabez Dawes,
His character was full of flaws.
In school he never led his classes,
He hid old ladies' reading glasses,
His mouth was open when he chewed,
And elbows to the table glued.

He stole the milk of hungry kittens,
And walked through doors marked NO ADMITTANCE.
He said he acted thus because
There wasn't any Santa Claus.
Another trick that tickled Jabez
Was crying "Boo!" at little babies.
He brushed his teeth, they said in town,
Sideways instead of up and down.

Yet people pardoned every sin,
And viewed his antics with a grin,
Till they were told by Jabez Dawes,
"There isn't any Santa Claus!"
Deploring how he did behave,
His parents swiftly sought their grave.
They hurried through the portals pearly,
And Jabez left the funeral early.

Like whooping cough, from child to child,
He sped to spread the rumor wild:
"Sure as my name is Jabez Dawes
There isn't any Santa Claus!"
Slunk like a weasel or a marten
Through nursery and kindergarten,
Whispering low to every tot,
"There isn't any, no there's not!"

The children wept all Christmas Eve
And Jebez chortled up his sleeve.
No infant dared hang up his stocking
For fear of Jabez' ribald mocking.
He sprawled on his untidy bed,
Fresh malice dancing in his head,
When presently with scalp a-tingling,
Jabez heard a distant jingling;
He heard the crunch of sleigh and hoof
Crisply alighting on the roof.

What good to rise and bar the door?
A shower of soot was on the floor.
What was beheld by Jabez Dawes?
The fireplace full of Santa Claus!
Then Jabez fell upon his knees
With cries of "Don't," and "Pretty please."
He howled, "I don't know where you read it,
But anyhow, I never said it!"

"Jabez," replied the angry saint,
"It isn't I, it's you that ain't.
Although there is a Santa Claus,
There isn't any Jabez Dawes!"
Said Jabez then with impudent vim,
"Oh, yes there is; and I am him!
Your magic don't scare me, it doesn't"—
And suddenly he found he wasn't!

From grimy feet to unkempt locks
Jabez became a jack-in-the-box,
An ugly, vastly ghastly jack
In Santa Claus's bulging pack.
The neighbors heard his mournful squeal;
They searched for him, but not with zeal.
No trace was found of Jabez Dawes,
Which led to thunderous applause,
And people drank a loving cup
And went and hung their stockings up.

All you who sneer at Santa Claus,
Beware the fate of Jabez Dawes,
The saucy boy who mocked the saint.
Donder and Blitzen licked off his paint.

OGDEN NASH

Sisyphus

Joy of the springtime! How the sun
Smiled on the hills of Burlington.

The breath of May! And the day was fair,
The bright motes danced in the balmy air.

The sunlight gleamed where the restless breeze
Kissed the fragrant blooms on the apple trees.

His beardless cheek with a smile was spanned
As he stood with a carriage whip in his hand.

Lightly he laughed as he doffed his coat
And the echoing folds of the carpet smote.

She smiled as she leaned on her busy mop,
And said she would tell him when to stop.

So he larruped away till the dinner bell
Gave him a little breathing spell.

But he sighed when the tardy clock struck one,
And she said that his carpet was most half done.

Yet he lovingly put in his liveliest licks,
And whipped like mad until half-past six.

When she said, in a dubious kind of way,
That she "guessed he could finish that side next day."

Then all that day, and the next day, too,
The fuzz from the dustless carpet flew.

And she'd give it a look at eventide,
And say, "Now whip on the other side."

So the new days came as the old days went,
And the landlord came for his regular rent.

While the neighbors laughed at the whup-zip-boom!
And his face grew shadowed with clouds of gloom.

Till at last, one dreary winter day,
Spurning his lifework, he fled away.

Over the fence and down the street,
Out into the Yon with footsteps fleet.

And never again did the morning sun
Smile on him beating his carpet drum.

Though sometimes a neighbor would say with a yawn—
"Where has the carpet martyr gone?"

*   *   *

Years twice twenty had come and passed
And the carpet moldered in sun and blast;

For never yet since that May grown old
Had hand been laid on its edge or fold.

Over the fence a gray-haired man,
Cautiously clim, clum, clem, clome, clam;

He found him a switch in the old woodpile
And he gathered it up with a sad, grim smile.

A flush passed over his face forlorn,
As he gazed at the carpet, stained and torn.

Then he struck it a most resounding thwack,
Till the startled air gave its echoes back.

Out of the window a white face leaned,
While a palsied hand the dim eyes screened.

At once she knew him—she gasped—she sighed—
"A little more on the under side!"

Right down on the ground his stick he throwed,
He shivered, and muttered—"Well, I am blowed!"

Then he turned him away with a heart full sore,
And he never was seen, not none, no more.

ROBERT J. BURDETTE

As Into the Garden

As into the garden Elizabeth ran
Pursued by the just indignation of Ann,
She trod on an object that lay in her road,
She trod on an object that looked like a toad.

It looked like a toad, and it looked so because
A toad was the actual object it was;
And after supporting Elizabeth's tread
It looked like a toad that was visibly dead.

Elizabeth, leaving her footprint behind,
Continued her flight on the wings of the wind,
And Ann in her anger was heard to arrive
At the toad that was not any longer alive.

She was heard to arrive, for the firmament rang
With the sound of a scream and the noise of a bang,
As her breath on the breezes she broadly bestowed
And fainted away on Elizabeth's toad.

Elizabeth, saved by the sole of her boot,
Escaped her insensible sister's pursuit;
And if ever hereafter she irritates Ann,
She will tread on a toad if she possibly can.

A. E. HOUSMAN

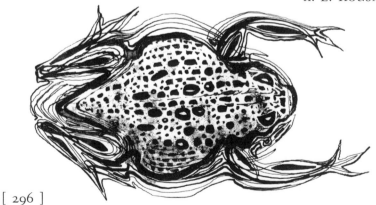

The Priest and the Mulberry Tree

Did you hear of the curate who mounted his mare,
And merrily trotted along to the fair?
Of creature more tractable none ever heard;
In the height of her speed she would stop at a word;
But again with a word, when the curate said, "Hey,"
She put forth her mettle and galloped away.

As near to the gates of the city he rode,
While the sun of September all brilliantly glowed,
The good priest discovered, with eyes of desire,
A mulberry tree in a hedge of wild brier;
On boughs long and lofty, in many a green shoot,
Hung, large, black, and glossy, the beautiful fruit.

The curate was hungry and thirsty to boot;
He shrunk from the thorns, though he longed for the fruit;
With a word he arrested his courser's keen speed,
And he stood up erect on the back of his steed;
On the saddle he stood while the creature stood still,
And he gather'd the fruit till he took his good fill.

"Sure never," he thought, "was a creature so rare,
So docile, so true, as my excellent mare;
Lo, here now I stand," and he gazed all around,
"As safe and as steady as if on the ground;
Yet how had it been, if some traveler this way,
Had, dreaming no mischief, but chanced to cry, 'Hey'?"

He stood with his head in the mulberry tree,
And he spoke out aloud in his fond revery;
At the sound of the word the good mare made a push,
And down went the priest in the wild-brier bush.
He remembered too late, on his thorny green bed,
Much that well may be thought cannot wisely be said.

THOMAS LOVE PEACOCK

Paddy O'Rafther

Paddy, in want of a dinner one day,
Credit all gone, and no money to pay,
Stole from a priest a fat pullet, they say,
    And went to confession just afther;
"Your riv'rince," says Paddy, "I stole this fat hen."
"What, what!" says the priest. "At your ould thricks again?
Faith, you'd rather be staalin' than sayin' *amen*,
                            Paddy O'Rafther!"

"Sure, you wouldn't be angry," says Pat, "if you knew
That the best of intintions I had in my view—
For I stole it to make it a present to you,
    And you can absolve me afther."
"Do you think," says the priest, "I'd partake of your theft?
Of your seven small senses you must be bereft—
You're the biggest blackguard that I know, right and left,
                            Paddy O'Rafther."

"Then what shall I do with the pullet," says Pat,
"If your riv'rince won't take it? By this and by that
I don't know no more than a dog or a cat
    What your riv'rince would have me be afther."
"Why, then," says his rev'rence, "you sin-blinded owl,
Give back to the man that you stole from his fowl:
For if you do not, 'twill be worse for your sowl,
                            Paddy O'Rafther!"

Says Paddy, "I ask'd him to take it—'tis thrue
As this minit I'm talkin', your riv'rince, to you;
But he wouldn't resaive it—so what can I do?"
    Says Paddy, nigh choken with laughter.
"By my throth," says the priest, "but the case is absthruse;
If he won't take his hen, why the man is a goose:
'Tis not the first time my advice was no use,
                            Paddy O'Rafther."

"But, for sake of your sowl, I would sthrongly advise
To someone in want you would give your supplies—
Some widow, or orphan, with tears in their eyes;
    And *then* you may come to *me* afther."
So Paddy went off to the brisk Widow Hoy,
And the pullet between them was eaten with joy,
And, says she, " 'Pon my word you're the cleverest boy,
                                Paddy O'Rafther."

Then Paddy went back to the priest the next day,
And told him the fowl he had given away
To a poor lonely widow, in want and dismay,
    The loss of her spouse weeping afther.
"Well, now," says the priest, "I'll absolve you, my lad,
For repentantly making the best of the bad,
In feeding the hungry and cheering the sad,
                                Paddy O'Rafther!"

SAMUEL LOVER

The Perils of Invisibility

Old Peter led a wretched life—
Old Peter had a furious wife;
Old Peter, too, was truly stout,
He measured several yards about.

The little fairy Picklekin
One summer afternoon looked in,
And said, "Old Peter, how-de-do?
Can I do anything for you?

"I have three gifts—the first will give
Unbounded riches while you live;
The second, health where'er you be;
The third, invisibility."

"O, little fairy Picklekin,"
Old Peter answered, with a grin,
"To hesitate would be absurd—
Undoubtedly I choose the third."

" 'Tis yours," the fairy said. "Be quite
Invisible to mortal sight
Whene'er you please. Remember me
Most kindly, pray, to Mrs. P."

Old Mrs. Peter overheard
Wee Picklekin's concluding word,
And, jealous of her girlhood's choice,
Said, "That was some young woman's voice!"

Old Peter let her scold and swear—
Old Peter, bless him, didn't care.
"My dear, your rage is wasted quite—
Observe, I disappear from sight!"

A well-bred fairy (so I've heard)
Is always faithful to her word:
Old Peter vanished like a shot,
But then—*his suit of clothes did not.*

For when conferred the fairy slim
Invisibility on him,
She popped away on fairy wings,
Without referring to his "things."

So there remained a coat of blue,
A vest and double eyeglass too,
His tail, his shoes, his socks as well,
His pair of—no, I must not tell.

Old Mrs. Peter soon began
To see the failure of his plan,

And then resolved (I quote the bard)
To "hoist him with his own petard."

Old Peter woke next day and dressed,
Put on his coat and shoes and vest,
His shirt and stock—*but could not find
His only pair of*—never mind!

Old Peter was a decent man,
And though he twigged his lady's plan,
Yet, hearing her approaching, he
Resumed invisibility.

"Dear Mrs. P., my only joy,"
Exclaimed the horrified old boy;
"Now give them up, I beg of you—
You know what I'm referring to!"

But no; the cross old lady swore
She'd keep his—what I said before—
To make him publicly absurd;
And Mrs. Peter kept her word.

The poor old fellow had no rest;
His coat, his stock, his shoes, his vest,
Were all that now met mortal eye—
The rest, invisibility!

"Now, madam, give them up, I beg—
I've bad rheumatics in my leg;
Besides, until you do, it's plain
I cannot come to sight again!

"For though some mirth it might afford
To see my clothes without their lord,
Yet there would rise indignant oaths
If he were seen without his clothes!"

But no; resolved to have her quiz,
The lady held her own—and his—
And Peter left his humble cot
To find a pair of—you know what.

But—here's the worst of this affair—
Whene'er he came across a pair
Already placed for him to don,
He was too stout to get them on!

So he resolved at once to train,
And walked and walked with all his main;
For years he paced this mortal earth,
To bring himself to decent girth.

At night, when all around is still,
You'll find him pounding up a hill;
And shrieking peasants whom he meets,
Fall down in terror on the peats!

Old Peter walks through wind and rain
Resolved to train, and train, and train,
Until he weighs twelve stone or so—
And when he does, I'll let you know.

W. S. GILBERT

The Blind Men and the Elephant

It was six men of Indostan
    To learning much inclined,
Who went to see the Elephant
    (Though all of them were blind),
That each by observation
    Might satisfy his mind.

The First approached the Elephant,
    And happening to fall
Against his broad and sturdy side,
    At once began to bawl:
"God bless me! but the Elephant
    Is very like a wall!"

The Second, feeling of the tusk,
    Cried, "Ho! what have we here
So very round and smooth and sharp?
    To me 'tis mighty clear
This wonder of an Elephant
    Is very like a spear!"

The Third approached the animal,
    And happening to take
The squirming trunk within his hands,
    Thus boldly up and spake:
"I see," quoth he, "the Elephant
    Is very like a snake!"

The Fourth reached out his eager hand,
    And felt about the knee.
"What most this wondrous beast is like
    Is mighty plain," quoth he;
" 'Tis clear enough the Elephant
    Is very like a tree!"

The Fifth, who chanced to touch the ear,
    Said: "E'en the blindest man
Can tell what this resembles most;
    Deny the fact who can,
This marvel of an Elephant
    Is very like a fan!"

The Sixth no sooner had begun
    About the beast to grope,

Than, seizing on the swinging tail
   That fell within his scope,
"I see," quoth he, "the Elephant
   Is very like a rope!"

And so these men of Indostan
   Disputed loud and long,
Each in his own opinion
   Exceeding stiff and strong,
Though each was partly in the right,
   And all were in the wrong!

Moral
So oft in theologic wars,
   The disputants, I ween,
Rail on in utter ignorance
   Of what each other mean,
And prate about an Elephant
Not one of them has seen!

JOHN GODFREY SAXE

The Snuffboxes

A village pedagogue announced one day
Unto his pupils, that Inspector A.
Was coming to examine them. Quoth he:
"If he should try you in Geography,
Most likely he will ask—'What's the Earth's shape?'
Then, if you feel as stupid as an ape,
Just look at me: my snuffbox I will show,
Which will remind you it is round, you know."

Now, the sagacious master, I declare,
Had two snuffboxes—one round, t'other square;

The square he carried through the week, the round
On Sundays only.
          Hark! a footstep's sound:
'Tis the Inspector. "What's the Earth's shape, lad?"
Addressing one by name. The latter, glad
To have his memory helped, looked at the master;
When, piteous to relate, O sad disaster!
The pupil without hesitation says:
"Round, sir, on Sundays, square on other days."

ANONYMOUS

Matilda

WHO TOLD LIES, AND WAS BURNED TO DEATH

Matilda told such Dreadful Lies,
It made one Gasp and Stretch one's Eyes;
Her Aunt, who, from her Earliest Youth,
Had kept a Strict Regard for Truth,
Attempted to Believe Matilda:
The effort very nearly killed her,
And would have done so, had not She
Discovered this Infirmity.
For once, towards the Close of Day,
Matilda, growing tired of play,
And finding she was left alone,
Went tiptoe to the Telephone
And summoned the Immediate Aid
Of London's Noble Fire Brigade.
Within an hour the Gallant Band
Were pouring in on every hand,
From Putney, Hackney Downs, and Bow.
With Courage high and Hearts a-glow,
They galloped, roaring through the Town,
"Matilda's House is Burning Down!"

Inspired by British Cheers and Loud
Proceeding from the Frenzied Crowd,
They ran their ladders through a score
Of windows on the Ball Room Floor;
And took Peculiar Pains to Souse
The Pictures up and down the House,
Until Matilda's Aunt succeeded
In showing them they were not needed;
And even then she had to pay
To get the Men to go away!

It happened that a few Weeks later
Her Aunt was off to the Theatre
To see that Interesting Play
The Second Mrs. Tanqueray.
She had refused to take her Niece
To hear this Entertaining Piece:
A Deprivation Just and Wise
To Punish her for Telling Lies.
That Night a Fire *did* break out—
You should have heard Matilda Shout!
You should have heard her Scream and Bawl,
And throw the window up and call
To the People passing in the Street—
(The rapidly increasing Heat
Encouraging her to obtain
Their confidence)—but all in vain!
For every time she shouted "Fire!"
They only answered "Little Liar!"
And therefore when her Aunt returned,
Matilda, and the House, were Burned.

HILAIRE BELLOC

Fable
of the Transcendent Tannenbaum

A
Tannen-
baum
whose secret
Traum
had been to be
a Christmas tree
was ground up in a paper mill
he took this very hard
until
he found himself
transcendently
a page
of Christmas
p
o
e
t
r
y

SCOTT BATES

The Sad Tale of Mr. Mears

There was a man who had a clock,
　His name was Matthew Mears;
And every day he wound that clock
　For eight and twenty years.

And then one day he found that clock
　An eight-day clock to be,
And a madder man than Matthew Mears
　You would not wish to see.

ANONYMOUS

The Owl Critic

"Who stuffed that white owl?" No one spoke in the shop:
The barber was busy, and he couldn't stop;
The customers, waiting their turns, were all reading
The *Daily,* the *Herald,* the *Post,* little heeding
The young man who blurted out such a blunt question;
Not one raised a head, or even made a suggestion;
　　　And the barber kept on shaving.

"Don't you see, Mister Brown,"
Cried the youth, with a frown,
"How wrong the whole thing is,
How preposterous each wing is,
How flattened the head is, how jammed down the neck is—
In short, the whole owl, what an ignorant wreck 'tis!
I make no apology;
I've learned owl-eology.
I've passed days and nights in a hundred collections,
And cannot be blinded to any deflections
Arising from unskillful fingers that fail

To stuff a bird right, from his beak to his tail.
Mister Brown! Mister Brown!
Do take that bird down,
Or you'll soon be the laughingstock all over town!"
        And the barber kept on shaving.

"I've studied owls
And other night fowls,
And I tell you
What I know to be true!
An owl cannot roost
With his limbs so unloosed;
No owl in this world
Ever had his claws curled,
Ever had his legs slanted,
Ever had his bill canted,
Ever had his neck screwed
Into that attitude.
He can't *do* it, because
'Tis against all bird laws.
Anatomy teaches,
Ornithology preaches,
An owl has a toe
That *can't* turn out so!
I've made the white owl my study for years,
And to see such a job almost moves me to tears!
Mister Brown, I'm amazed
You should be so gone crazed
As to put up a bird
In that posture absurd!
To *look* at that owl really brings on a dizziness;
The man who stuffed *him* don't half know his business!"
        And the barber kept on shaving.

"Examine those eyes.
I'm filled with surprise
Taxidermists should pass

Off on you such poor glass;
So unnatural they seem
They'd make Audubon scream,
And John Burroughs laugh
To encounter such chaff.
Do take that bird down;
Have him stuffed again, Brown!"
                    And the barber kept on shaving.

"With some sawdust and bark
I would stuff in the dark
An owl better than that;
I could make an old bat
Look more like an owl
Than that horrid fowl,
Stuck up there so stiff like a side of coarse leather.
In fact, about *him* there's not one natural feather."

Just then, with a wink and a sly normal lurch,
The owl, very gravely, got down from his perch,
Walked round, and regarded his fault-finding critic
(Who thought he was stuffed) with a glance analytic,
And then fairly hooted, as if he should say:
"Your learning's at fault *this* time, anyway;
Don't waste it again on a live bird, I pray.
I'm an owl; you're another. Sir Critic, good day!"
                    And the barber kept on shaving.

JAMES THOMAS FIELDS

Old Wichet

I went into my stable, to see what I might see,
And there I saw three horses stand, by one, by two, by three.
I called unto my loving wife, and "Coming, sir!" said she,
"O what do these three horses here without the leave of me?"

"Why, old fool, blind fool! can't you very well see,
    That these are three milking cows my mother sent to me?"
"Hey, boys! Fill the cup! Milking cows with saddles up!
The like was never known, the like was never known."
Old Wichet went a noodle out, a noodle he came home.

I went into the kitchen, to sce what I might see,
And there I saw three swords hung up, by one, by two, by three.
I called unto my loving wife, and "Coming, sir!" said she,
"O why do these three swords hang here without the leave of me?"
    "Why, old fool, blind fool! can't you very well see,
    That these are three toasting forks my mother sent to me?"
"Hey, boys! Well done! Toasting forks with scabbards on!
The like was never known, the like was never known."
Old Wichet went a noodle out, a noodle he came home.

I went into the pantry, to see what I might see,
And there I saw three pairs of boots, by one, by two, by three.
I called unto my loving wife, and "Coming, sir!" said she,
"O what do these three pairs of boots without the leave of me?"
    "Why, old fool, blind fool! can't you very well see,
    That these are three pudding bags my mother sent to me?"
"Hey, boys! Well done! Pudding bags with steel spurs on!
The like was never known, the like was never known."
Old Wichet went a noodle out, a noodle he came home.

I went into the dairy, to see what I might see,
And there I saw three beavers, by one, by two, by three.
I called unto my loving wife, and "Coming, sir!" said she,
"O what do these three beavers here without the leave of me?"
    "Why, old fool, blind fool! can't you very well see,
    That these are three milking pails my mother sent to me?"
"Hey, boys! Well done! Milking pails with ribbons on!
The like was never known, the like was never known."
Old Wichet went a noodle out, a noodle he came home.

I went into the chamber, to see what I might see,
And there I saw three men in bed, by one, by two, by three.
I called unto my loving wife, and "Coming, sir!" said she,
"O why sleep here three gentlemen without the leave of me?"
    "Why, old fool, blind fool! can't you very well see,
    That these are three milking maids my mother sent to me?"
"Hey, boys! Well done! Milking maids with beards on!
The like was never known, the like was never known."
Old Wichet went a noodle out, a noodle he came home.

I went into the chamber, as quick as quick might be,
I kicked the three men down the stairs, by one, by two, by three.
"Without your hats and boots be off, your horses leave and flee,
Your purses 'neath your pillows left; they too belong to me.
    Why, old wife, blind wife! can't you very well see,
    That these are three highwaymen from justice hid by thee?
Hey, boys! Purses left! Knaves they be, and away are flown.
The like was never known, the like was never known."
Old Wichet went a noodle out, a wise man he came home.

OLD BALLAD

Index of Authors

Index of Titles

Index of First Lines